## ACTIVITY BOOK
## FOR STUDENTS AND TEACHERS

# *Thoughtsteps*

# Steps to Discovering Culture and Values

KARINA YOUNK

Art Image Publications

***Thoughtsteps*** is an intermediate learning resource based on the integration of language arts, science, and social studies, along with other subject areas and processing skills, whenever there are natural links. ***Thoughtsteps*** can be used with the entire class, with small groups, with individual students, or as a learning centre.

**EDITORS**
Joan Irving
Catherine Stewart
André Vandal

**STUDENT EDITORS**
Alexandre Fallon
Shannon Provencher

**ILLUSTRATORS**
François Thisdale
Pierre Massé

**PILOT CLASSES**
Donna Anderson, Grade 6
Mount Benson Elementary, Nanaimo, BC

Paul Chetty, Grades 5 to 9
Miskooseepi School, Blood Vein River, MB

**CONSULTANTS IN MUSIC, ART, AND LITERATURE**
Sue Postans
Regan Rasmussen
Linda Irvine
Donna Klockars

© 1998 Beauchemin Publishing Group Ltd. / Art Image Publications, Inc.

ISBN: 1-896876-17-X

CANADA
Beauchemin Publishing Group/Art Image
Publications Inc.
3281 Jean-Beraud Avenue
Laval, QC
H7T 2L2
Tel: (514) 334-5912 • 1 800 361-2598
Fax: 1 800 559-2598

USA
Art Image Publications Inc.
P.O. Box 568
Champlain, NY 12919
Tel: 1 800 361-2598
Fax: 1 800 559-2598

Printed in Canada

# Thoughtsteps

**SO YOU'RE GETTING READY TO WANDER THROUGH THOUGHTSTEPS?**

Before you start, check out these pieces of information:
p. 5 – The parts of *Thoughtsteps*.
p. 6 – Using the *Thoughtsteps Map* and *Thoughtsteps Planner*.
p. 7 – The *Steps to Discovering...* activities: Preparing your *Thoughtsteps Journal*.

## PARTS OF THOUGHTSTEPS

First, let's look at the six components or parts of *Thoughtsteps*. You prepare one part (your journal or notebook) yourself and the other five parts are provided for you in the centres. These six components are:

1. The *Thoughtsteps Journal* is your personal binder containing your projects, notes, written work, experiments, evaluations, and more. The journal becomes your record of what you accomplish and learn as you work through the centres and themes in *Thoughtsteps*.

2. The *Thoughtsteps Map* is a map showing the different paths or options that a learner may choose. The map may seem confusing if you try to read the whole thing at once, but if you follow one path from start to finish, you'll soon understand how the map works.

3. The *Thoughtsteps Planner* is a folder containing a summary of the concepts and skills you will be learning in each theme of a centre. Its purpose is to help you determine which activities you will be doing as a class, as a small group, or as

an individual. It is like an itinerary for a trip, which tells you in advance what you will be expected to collect, learn, or observe for each part of your journey. It can also help you with your evaluation of the theme, and what you learned. At the end of each activity, you will review the objectives and ask yourself if you have accomplished what you set out to do.

4. The *Thoughtsteps Toolbox* contains a series of cards with information and evaluation notes designed to help you learn HOW to do something.

5. *Steps to Discovering...* is a guide for working your way through the projects and activities contained in each centre or theme. When you read through your *Steps to Discovering...* activities, you'll choose a path and follow the suggestions along the way. *Steps* will help you decide WHAT to do, WHERE to look, WHO you're working with (alone, in a group, or as a class), WHEN you need to record information, and WHY you're doing the activity. Like a tour book, it helps you pick and choose not only your destination but also what you plan to do along the way. Like any tour, you might like to "go it alone", travel with a friend, or have someone, like your teacher or a group leader, help you plan your way.

6. *Discovering Wind and Water; Discovering Culture and Values; Discovering the Earth's Crust; Discovering Space* are some of the resource books in the *Thoughtsteps* series. They contain stories, poems, artwork, projects, experiments, and much more, to give you a starting point for information on the centres and themes.

### USING THE THOUGHTSTEPS MAP AND THE THOUGHTSTEPS PLANNER

Have you ever juggled before? Juggling one or two objects is easy. Juggling more objects takes skill and practice. Once you know how *Thoughtsteps* works, you'll be able to juggle its components easily.

**Thoughtsteps is set up so that you take one step at a time. Just follow the directions listed below.**

> **N.B.** To be ready to discuss the centre as a group, post the *Thoughtsteps Map* in a place where it will stay for the duration of your work with this centre. Have the group members sit so that they can see the *Thoughtsteps Map*. Distribute the *Thoughtsteps Planners* – the folders for the themes in the centre – to each member of the group.

1. Look at the *Thoughtsteps Map*. What is the name of the centre you will be working in: *Discovering Wind and Water*; *Discovering Space*; or *Discovering...*?

2. Each *Thoughtsteps* centre contains two or more options for themes and a culminating Cooperative Project integrating the activities from all the themes. For example, in *Discovering Wind and Water*, the choices are: air; weather; water. What are your options in the centre you have chosen? What would you like to learn about? Below each option on the *Thoughtsteps Map* is the title of the theme. For now, find the title of the Cooperative Project.

3. Below each theme on the *Thoughtsteps Map* are several titles for the different learning *paths* that you may follow. Follow the path below the Cooperative Project.

4. What do you need to do to prepare for this path? Check the **preparation section** of your *Thoughtsteps Map*. What are you expected to learn? The *Thoughtsteps*

*Planner* describes the learning objectives for each theme and subject area. Check the preparation objectives 𝒫 for the Cooperative Project.

5. What will you be producing or doing? Check the **action or activity section** of your map. Check your *Thoughtsteps Planner* for the activity objectives 𝒜.

6. What are your options for extending the activity? Check the **extension section** of the map. These objectives aren't listed beside 𝐸 in your *Thoughtsteps Planner*, but if you select one of these activities, your teacher has a list of the objectives in the *Educator's Planner*.

7. What are you asked to think about or reflect on at the end of your activity? Check the **reflection section** of your map and the reflection objectives 𝑅 in your *Thoughtsteps Planner*.

8. When you are ready to work on a path, refer to the appropriate *Steps to Discovering...* activity book. It contains all the information you will need (explanations for the activities, the *Toolbox* cards, etc.). The **STEPS...** page is indicated below each path title on the *Thoughtsteps Map*. If you are planning to do a Cooperative Project, consult the pages in your *Steps to Discovering...* book now. You will need to complete the preparation stage of this project before planning your other activities for this centre.

9. Once you have examined the *Thoughtsteps Map* and the Cooperative Project, select the activities you will do as a whole class, in small groups, or individually. Mark your *Thoughtsteps Planner* accordingly: **C; G; I**. If there are activities that you won't be doing in class, you may decide to do these on your own. Mark these in your *Planner* as well.

# STEPS TO DISCOVERING... ACTIVITIES

### Preparing your *Thoughtsteps Journal*

# Beyond Folklore

 Open your *Thoughtsteps Journal*. Add to it a blank page, a lined page, and two more blank pages.
- On the first page, write the title of your theme.
- On the lined page, write the words "Table of Contents". As you work through the theme, list your activities here.
- On the next blank page, list your ideas, words, knowledge relating to First Nations in North America. See **Tool A2**.

 Using your list of ideas from the brainstorming activity, make a poster on the next page of your *Thoughtsteps Journal*. Show words and images about the theme *Discovering Culture and Values:* **Beyond Folklore**.

On the back of this page, write the title "Discovering New Words". As you work through the activities in this theme, list on this page any new words you encounter.

**.1** Use a dictionary to review spelling.

**Or**

**.2** Create a class poster combining everyone's ideas.

**Or**

**.3** Look through other resource books for ideas for illustrations or words. Add them to your poster.

**Or**

**.4** Add illustrations to your title page.

**Or**

**.5** Add a **Bibliography** page. See **Tool A5** to learn how to list your sources.

 Check your poster for spelling: remember it's a tool you will use during the entire theme! Does it represent the theme? At the bottom of the poster, write down three ideas you would like to explore in this theme.

## A

### Beyond Folklore

### A.1

*Needs and Environment*

LA: Identify/use information from ideas to express a point of view, an opinion, or an analysis.
SS: Understand that human activity involves satisfying basic needs and affects the environment.

Using **Tools A2** and **A3,** make a list of ideas about the basic survival needs of humans and animals. Group these ideas into categories and write them on a chart like this:

| HUMANS NEED | ANIMALS NEED |
|---|---|
| food | food |
| shelter | shelter, etc. |

Refer to the needs identified in the chart above to discuss the following ideas (and any new ideas that you may have):

- What would happen if there were a drought (if it didn't rain for a very long time)?

- What would happen if there were no wood for building homes?

- How are animals and humans dependent on their environment?

- How do we satisfy our basic needs within our environment?

In the following activity, you will be constructing graphs to illustrate your findings. For additional practice with graphing, refer to relevant exercises in your math textbook.

LA: Recognize that visuals may contain bias.
Sc: Understand the relationships between living organisms and the environment.
SS: Understand that human activity involves satisfying basic needs and affects the environment.
Ma: Construct/interpret graphs to represent data collected and to classify information.

To learn about how living things depend on their environment, play a survival game simulating the relationship between animals and the fulfillment of their basic needs. The explanation for this game is given on **STEPSpage 11**.

Using **Tool A1**, discuss how you felt about the game and what you observed about the changes in the animal populations. Present the results of the game on a graph using the data gathered during the game. See **Tool D5** for help on how to construct and read a graph.

Answer the questions on **STEPSpages 12 and 13**.

**E.1** LA: Recognize that visuals may contain bias.
SS: Understand that human activity involves satisfying basic needs and affects the environment.
Ma: Construct/interpret graphs to represent data collected and to classify information.

Prepare a graph to show how rapidly species are becoming extinct.
See **STEPSpage 14** and **Tool D5**.

Or

**E.2** SS: Understand that human activity involves satisfying basic needs and affects the environment.
FA: Experiment with a collage to represent plants and/or animals.

Design a collage about endangered species. See **STEPSpage 16** and **Tool D3**.

Or

**E.3** LA: Experiment with interviews as a means of expressing a point of view or an opinion.
SS: Understand that human activity involves satisfying basic needs and affects the environment.

Simulate an interview between a person and an endangered species. See
**STEPSpage 17** and **Tool B4**.

Or

**E.4** SS: Understand that human activity involves satisfying basic needs and affects the environment.
FA: Use colour, shade, and shape in a mobile to create equilibrium.

Design a hanging mobile to show how living organisms try to keep the balance
in their ecosystem. See **STEPSpage 18** and **Tool D3**.

Or

**E.5** SS: Understand how humans attempt to make sense of their environment through exploration.
FA: Formulate a monologue from a given theme. Use appropriate gestures, voice,
and special effects.

Prepare a visualization exercise on harmony in nature to describe one of your
favourite outside places. See **STEPSpage 19** and **Tool B3**.

Or

**E.6** SS: Understand how humans attempt to make sense of their environment through exploration.
FA: Use the space available according to number of players and intent of actions.

Create a dance that would simulate harmony in nature.
See **STEPSpage 20** and **Tool D8**.

**A**
Beyond
Folklore

**A.1**
*Needs
and
Environment*

# A

## Beyond Folklore

## A.1
### Needs and Environment

SD: Understand the importance of change to groups as a means for growth as a society. Identify, develop, and sustain means of improving expression and effective communication.

In your **Thoughtsteps Journal**, write one or more paragraphs to summarize the main messages of this learning path. Before you start writing, read and think about the following questions.

1. How does your society or cultural group meet its basic needs? Can you think of a society that meets its needs differently? Give two examples to compare these differences.

2. Is your society's population increasing or decreasing? What effect will this change have on the environment? In your opinion, how do human populations impact on the ecosystem's balancing act?

3. What does your society take from the environment? What does it give back? Is the relationship between taking and giving an equal one? Do you know of other societies that have a better way to achieve this balance?

4. Do you think that your society is living in equilibrium with nature? If not, what changes would you suggest? (Think about other societies that you have studied. Do these societies have something to teach our society?)

There are many different species on this planet. Human societies have a choice. Will each society respect and value its relationship with the earth and with other living things? Or will it choose to control and dominate the earth's resources to serve only its own needs? Which society would you prefer?

Complete the evaluations from **Tools A1** and **D5**.

# IT'S A GAME OF SURVIVAL!

Play a survival game to learn about animals in their environment.

*Divide the players into two groups as follows:*

One out of four of the players will represent a particular animal population (e.g., deer). The game is to show how a single animal population changes, so it is important that the group represents only one kind of animal.
Three out of four of the players will represent the basic needs (food, water, shelter) of this animal population.

### DIRECTIONS

1. Decide on the boundaries of the game. The "animal population" group lines up along one end of the playing area. The "food, water, shelter" group representing the animals' basic needs lines up at the other end of the playing area (15-20 metres away). Both groups turn their backs so they can't see each other.

2. On the first signal, each of the players from both groups chooses a hand position:

   "food" – place one hand on your stomach;

   "water" – place one hand over your mouth;

   "shelter" – place one hand on your head.

3. On the second signal, the two groups quickly turn to face each other showing the opposite group which basic need they want (the animals) or they represent (the basic needs). Each of the "animals" races to catch one of the "basic needs" players showing the hand position that matches theirs.

4. An "animal" captures only one "basic need" and returns to the start line with its capture. This animal is presumed to have survived and was able to have young babies in the next season (so the captured "basic need" now becomes another "animal"). Any animal who does not succeed in satisfying its basic needs is presumed to have died of thirst, hunger, or cold. These players go to join the "basic needs" group behind their line.

5. The teacher plays the role of the biologist or zoologist by counting and recording the number of animals after each "season".

**IT'S A GAME OF SURVIVAL!**, continued...

6. The next round or season starts when the leader asks the new groups to line up again, with their backs to each other, and to choose a sign.

7. The game should be repeated at least 15 times to gather data over the lifetime of the animal. Be sure to count the animal population at the end of each round.

At the end of the game, your chart might look like this:

| SEASON | NUMBER OF ANIMALS |
|--------|-------------------|
| 1st | 7 |
| 2nd | 12 |
| 3rd | 10... etc. |

Present the results of the game on a graph using the data gathered during the game. See **Tool D5** for help on how to construct and interpret a graph.

After the game, answer the following questions in your *Thoughtsteps Journal* and then discuss your answers with a group of students.

*While you were playing the survival game:*

1. Was it easier for a small group or for a large group of animals to satisfy their needs within the same environment?

2. As the animal population in a given environment increases, what happens to the supply of food, water, and shelter?

3. How does a decrease in food, water, and/or shelter affect the animal population?

4. How does nature maintain a state of equilibrium among animal populations?

5. Do the same rules apply to humans? Have we changed the rules? How? Think about the ways in which humans protect their food, water, and shelter (fences, irrigation, security systems, pesticides).

**IT'S A GAME OF SURVIVAL!,** continued...

**A**
Beyond
Folklore

**A.1**
*Needs
and
Environment*

*Looking at the graph that you made:*

1. How might you explain the changes (fluctuations) in your graph?

2. Could the fluctuations (changes) in your graph also apply to humans?

3. What would happen if there was no more drinking water available on Earth?

*Extending the game to human societies:*

1. How did the first humans on this planet meet their needs? (Inuit peoples may patiently hunt for food under the sea ice, while Amazon Tupi peoples could easily find their food in the rich plants and creatures of the jungle.)

2. Over time, how have societies changed the ways in which they meet their needs? Imagine what your life would be like if nobody farmed anymore. How has the invention of gunpowder helped hunters? Why do some cultures not allow consumption of certain foods? (Muslims don't eat pork, cows are sacred in India, you would probably never eat a dog or a cat.)

3. Do you think that humans should be concerned about natural resources?

4. Is it possible that humans might one day be on the endangered species list? What would be the causes?

5. If you were to invent a game that demonstrates the relationship between humans and how we meet our needs, how would it differ from this survival game?

6. What do we have to consider in order to be sure that we will always be able to satisfy our basic needs?

## A

### Beyond Folklore

### A.1

### *Needs and Environment*

 .1 GRAPHING THE RAPID RATE OF SPECIES EXTINCTION

Prepare a graph to show how rapidly species are becoming extinct.

**BACKGROUND INFORMATION**

For the past 3.6 billion years, animal species have been disappearing. They vanish or slowly die out because they are not able to adapt to their environment. From the study of fossil records, scientists have estimated that one species may have naturally died out every 1000 years. In today's conditions, scientists estimate that one species would likely become extinct every 27 years. However, with human activity encroaching upon or destroying more and more of the natural habitat, over 1300 identified species are being monitored because they are in danger of extinction! Between the years 1600 and 1900, one animal species became extinct every four years. Between 1900 and 1985, the estimated rate increased to 3.5 species disappearing every four years. Today, the World Wildlife Fund estimates that, due to the rapid rate of rainforest destruction, one plant or animal species is lost every hour (over 8000 every year). Of the 20 to 30 million species, half live in the tropical rainforests. Therefore, depletion of our forests has a direct effect on the biodiversity of this planet.

Using **Tool D5**, prepare a graph showing the number of animal species that became extinct between 1600 and 1985. Then extrapolate to include the estimates of extinction rates after 1985.

– What can you learn by looking at the graph?

– How many animal species became extinct between 1600 and 1900?

– How many species disappeared between 1900 and 1985?

– What do you notice about the curve in your graph after 1985?

– What can be done to help endangered species?

– What does the information in your graph tell you about how humans value and respect their environment and the species in it?

**A**

**Beyond
Folklore**

**A.1**

*Needs
and
Environment*

*Stretch your thinking into actions!*

− Does your graph represent your views as to how you value and respect your environment? If it does not represent your views, what actions are you prepared to take to make changes happen?

− Does your graph represent your culture's views of the environment? What positive actions have been taken in your region to improve the plight of endangered species? (You could talk to a veterinarian, a conservation officer, a park warden, or other resource person to find the answer to the latter question.)

− The industrial era has had an immense impact on the environment. Traditional cultures and respect for the environment have been forgotten or ignored in the race to make humans' lives better, easier, more fulfilling. Technology has allowed us to make changes even more rapidly. But people are starting to ask, is this really the answer? No one really wants to go back to lighting fires in the pouring rain to cook the food caught that day. What are the alternatives? How can industry and technology be used to change the statistics shown on this graph? The media provide us with many examples of success stories in environmental fields. For a week, check various information sources (newspaper, television, radio, magazines, Internet) to look for examples of success stories. Share them with your classmates.

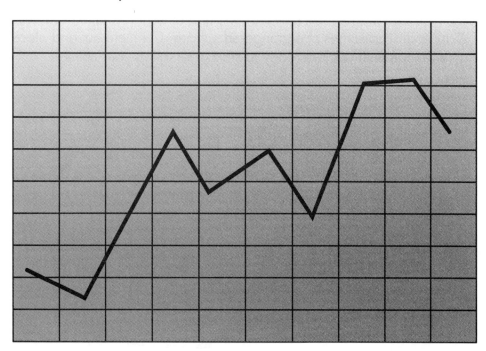

.2 ENDANGERED SPECIES ALERT!

Design a collage that represents endangered species in your region, your country, or on the planet. On the collage, attempt to identify the causes of the phenomenon and possible solutions or actions. What influences do modern societies have on animal and plant species? Is this influence more obvious in some societies or in some cultural regions than in others?

Use **Tool D3** to help you organize the collage and evaluate it when you're done. Here is some information to get you started:

**BACKGROUND INFORMATION**

With the arrival of the industrial and agricultural revolutions, hundreds of species of animals have vanished from Earth. In this century alone, more than 8000 plant and animal species are estimated to have disappeared forever. Human destruction of animal habitats is seen as one of the major reasons. Here is the definition of a species in danger of extinction:
"Each and every species whose existence within its natural habitat is threatened by human actions."

To receive a list of endangered species in Canada, write to the following address:

**Committee on the Status of
Endangered Wildlife in Canada
Environment Canada, Department of Wildlife
Distribution Centre
Ottawa, Ontario
K1A 0E7**

Look through magazines, newspapers, and other information sources to find pictures or illustrations of endangered species. Cut them out and place them in an envelope until you are ready to start assembling your collage.

# E.3 PERSONAL INTERVIEWS WITH ENDANGERED SPECIES

**A**

Beyond
Folklore

**A.1**

*Needs
and
Environment*

With a friend, simulate an interview between a person and an endangered species. Practise on your own, then do the final interview in front of your class. The purpose of this interview is to inform listeners how animals might feel in their desperation to survive and to find out why animals are becoming extinct. The interview questions should focus on which basic needs are not being met for this particular animal population. Why are these needs not being met?

1. Use **Tool A4** to develop a list of questions that might be asked by the human or by the animal. Think about the animal's basic needs: food, water, shelter, and rest. Ask questions, too, that would help listeners understand the animal's emotions when it cannot meet its basic needs.

2. Select the questions you wish to keep for your interview. Write these questions onto cue cards, one set for the endangered species being interviewed and the other for the human interviewer. Be sure to check your punctuation!

3. Choose a background for your interview. Decide what your costumes will be.

4. Practise your interview several times before presenting it. Use **Tools B1** and **B4** to evaluate your interview both before and after you present it. You might want to ask your teacher to videotape your interview.

5. Think of questions to ask your audience after the interview to find out what they learned, what they think, etc. Be prepared to act as the leader of the discussion.

# E.4 BALANCING BASIC NEEDS

Design a hanging mobile to demonstrate how animals need to find a state of balance by meeting their basic needs. See **Tool D3** for ideas on how to prepare your mobile and how to evaluate it.

1. Begin by selecting an animal. Find a picture of this animal or draw it. Glue your animal picture on a piece of rigid paper or cardboard and trim the edges.

2. Illustrate each of the animal's basic needs: water, food, shelter, and environment. Glue these illustrations on separate pieces of cardboard.

3. Attach a string 10 cm long to each piece of the mobile. Assemble the mobile with the animal and its basic needs as illustrated below:

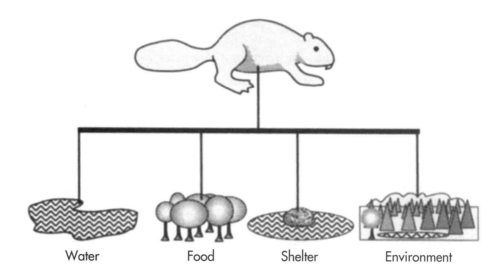

Water          Food          Shelter          Environment

4. Gently blow or push your mobile. What happens to the different parts of the mobile? Nature is contantly changing. However, these changes tend to balance out so that the ecosystem appears to remain balanced.

5. What would happen if you were to remove one of the elements from the mobile? Would your mobile stay balanced? Does such imbalance occur in real life? What actions are being taken to prevent the extinction of the species represented in your mobile?

6. How does your mobile show why some animals are in danger of extinction? What other presentation formats could you have used to illustrate a state of equilibrium or balance in nature?

7. Based on what you have learned in this extension activity, in what simple ways could you demonstrate that you value and respect your environment and the ecosystem in which you live?

**E.5** VISUALIZING A FAVOURITE PLACE

Prepare a visualization exercise on harmony in nature to describe one of your favourite outside places.

1. Read the information in **Tool B1**. Then choose your favourite outdoor place or activity and write a description of it. For example, describe a walk in the forest, a bike trip along a mountain trail or a swim in the lake. Include details about the scenery, the smells, the textures, and so on so that your friends will be able to imagine this place in their minds. Think about which adjectives you could add to better describe this place. See **Tool E2**. Here is an example for you:

> *Imagine that you are in a forest. Listen to the sound of your footsteps on the trail. Listen to the birds singing among the branches. Watch them fly from the branches into the blue sky overhead. Smell the fresh air of the forest. Smell the fragrances of the forest flowers and plants. Feel the cool breeze on your face. Bend down and touch the moist, rich soil. Watch a snail as it slowly creeps its way along a slender twig…*

2. Choose a selection of music that fits well with your description. See **Tool B3**.

3. Ask your friends to lie down on a carpet, or on the mats in the gym, or simply to place their heads on their desks. Let them know that they will hear soft music and that you will be reading them a description of your favourite place. Tell them to close their eyes and relax their muscles from their heads to their toes. As you start the music, be sure that you are relaxed, too! Keep your voice strong, but soft. Be sure to read your description slowly!

4. When you are finished, ask your friends to open their eyes when they are ready. Take a few minutes to talk about how they felt, what they saw, and what they thought about the visualization exercise. Use **Tools B1** and **B3** to evaluate your visualization exercise.

A

Beyond

Folklore

A.1

Needs
and
Environment

# E.6 CREATE A DANCE TO SIMULATE HARMONY IN NATURE

Use your visualization exercise from **Extension E.5** as a starting point, or start with a new idea. This activity can be done alone or with a group. **Tool D8** offers ideas on how to present your dance.

1. Begin by discussing what movements each dancer could make to show that he or she is reaching out to nature. One person may begin with a simple movement. Another person can add a movement. Continue experimenting until everyone has had a chance to demonstrate one or more movements.

2. What music could you use? Perhaps there's a song you would like to compose or one that you know already. Listen to the music several times. Divide your selection of music into segments.

3. Represent your dance on paper so that you can visualize the combined movements. Begin by drawing a large circle for each segment of music. In the first circle, mark an "X" to show where each of the dancers will be at the start of the dance. Use a different coloured pencil for each dancer. With a dotted arrow, indicate where each dancer will move during the first segment of music. At the end of this dotted arrow, draw a dotted "X" to show where each dancer will be at the end of the segment of music. At the end of the first movement, are the positions of the dancers still evenly balanced? Remember that nature is constantly changing, but that these changes seem to balance out in the end.

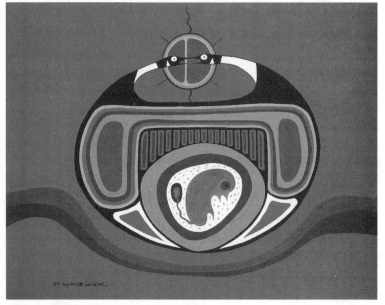

Jackson Beardy, *Rebirth*

4. In each of the other circles, represent the movement of the dancers for that segment of music. For each segment of your dance, there should be evidence of change, imbalance, and then balance. Use the space beside each circle to write a brief explanation of the body movements used by the dancers in representing their idea of harmony in nature.

5. Practise the dance several times so that everyone knows their movements well. Ask someone to watch your dance to adjust your spacing, if needed, and also to make suggestions for smoother movements throughout the dance.

6. Think of appropriate costumes to wear. If you could use special lighting effects, how would you use them?

Crouch down, head on thighs, arms relaxed, pointing towards toes. Rise slowly, like a plant growing, reach with one arm and move in direction of that arm.

When you are ready and have practised your dance several times, present it to a group of friends or to your class. Evaluate your dance using **Tool D8**.

# A

## Beyond Folklore

### A.2

#### *Following the Paths to the Future*

LA: Identify/use information from a text/image to analyze details and to establish relationships.

SS: Understand that human activity involves satisfying basic needs. Interpret, construct, and use maps to represent human and physical characteristics.

FA: Experiment with drawings to represent mental images of people and certain facets of the environment.

SD: Recognize, examine, and appreciate individual/group differences in means of attaining a goal.

Read the poem **"The Journey"** on **page 5** in *Discovering Culture and Values*. This poem relates one theory of the possible journey of the first Inuit from Asia, across the Bering Strait, and into North America's Arctic regions. Use an atlas to locate the route that some people believe the first Inuit might have travelled from Asia to North America.

– Do you agree with this theory? Do you know of other theories? What do the legends of the Inuit people say about their origins? Where could you find this information? See **Tool A5**.

The poems on **pages 6** and **7** of *Discovering Culture and Values* highlight the traditional lifestyles of the Inuit people. The next two poems on **pages 8** and **9** give examples of how the lifestyles of the Inuit have changed. Using the information you gather from these poems and from other sources, create a map and illustrations to demonstrate your knowledge of First Nations of the northern regions. **STEPSpage 25** and **Tools D4** and **E10** give details on how to do this.

LA: Organize information logically and chronologically in a simple research report. Demonstrate an understanding of language conventions.

SS: Compare different events in time. Describe the effects of time. Study a milieu to identify and compare relationships between physical and human traits in the past, present, and possible future. Understand that communities and environment are interrelated.

SD: Identify, develop, and sustain means of improving individual/group value systems, attitudes, and resulting actions.

Using a variety of information sources, research what is known about the origins and lifestyles of First Nations peoples in your region. See **STEPSpage 26** for ideas on how to explore the traditional and modern lifestyles of First Nations peoples. To develop your research project, see **Tools C4** and **E9**. Use the same topics explored on **STEPSpage 25** of the preparation stage. Check your draft using **Tool C8**. Focus on your use of verbs in the past and present tense. Present your research in the form of a mural illustrating the transition from past to present (and future, if you like). See **Tool D3**.

**E.1** LA: Experiment with forms of poetry to organize selected ideas creatively. Identify/use information from a text/image to predict and extrapolate. Organize selected information creatively in a poem.

SS: Understand that human activity involves satisfying basic needs. Understand that communities and environment are interrelated.

Consult **Tool E5** to help you examine the different forms of poetry – haiku, cinquain, and diamante – on **pages 6** and **7** of **Discovering Culture and Values**. Then write a poem about the movement of peoples to explain why people might move to another place. Use **Tool C3** to get you started.

**Or**

**E.2** LA: Identify/use information from appropriate sources to analyze details and to establish relationships. Organize information logically and chronologically in a simple research report. Demonstrate an understanding of language conventions.

SS: Compare different events in time. Describe the effects of time. Understand that communities and environment are interrelated.

Add other aspects of traditional or contemporary life to your research project: art, religion (beliefs), customs, music, means of government, sports, leisure activities, and so on. For example, you could examine how community decisions were, or are, made or the roles art and music play in this society. **STEPSpage 28** gives a list of suggested topics.

**Or**

**E.3** LA: Identify/use information from a text to predict and extrapolate.

SS: Study a milieu to identify and compare relationships between physical and human traits in the past, present, and possible future.

Use an audiovisual presentation of your choice to demonstrate how global warming affects the traditional or contemporary (modern) Inuit lifestyle. See **STEPSpage 30**.

**Or**

**E.4** LA: Identify/use information from appropriate sources to analyze details and to establish relationships.

Research the origin and significance of First Nations' names for places or their names for famous leaders, explorers, women, and so on. See **STEPSpage 32**.

**A**
Beyond
Folklore

**A.2**
*Following
the Paths to
the Future*

Complete the evaluation forms from **Tools C4** and **D3**. Include them in your *Thoughtsteps Journal*. You might want to insert your project(s) or a picture of it (them). If you used other **Tools**, you may have other evaluation forms to add to your *Thoughtsteps Journal*.

# Mapping Past Paths

From the skeletons and artifacts that have been found, anthropologists (scientists who study human cultures) generally believe that the first humans on Earth lived in hot, dry places like in the Middle East, Northeastern Africa, Australia, East Asia, and Central and South America.

Before going on to the activity section, discuss the following questions.

- If the ancestors of the Inuit did come from East Asia, from what hot, dry area might they have originated?

- In your opinion, why would they choose to live and adapt to the harsh northern climate?

- Which other First Nations live in the Arctic region? In North America? Could they have emigrated here from another region? If so, where might they have come from?

- Do you think other First Nations have the same origins as the Inuit? Why? Why not?

- Who were the first known inhabitants in your region? What is known or believed about their origins?

Read the poems on **pages 6** and **7** of *Discovering Culture and Values*. In your *Thoughtsteps Journal*, record the information contained in the poems using a chart (see **Tool E9**) or mind map format (see **Tool A3**). List the details from the poems which describe:

- the climate and geography of the north;
- the type of shelters used at that time;
- the type of clothing worn then;
- the food the Inuit ate long ago;
- the means of transportation used.

Consult at least three other sources of information to add more detail to your mural. How do the illustrations in your mural compare with the poems and illustrations in *Discovering Culture and Values*?

If the Inuit were to have chosen to live in the prairies or the mountains, how would their lifestyles have been different? To answer this question, think about the First Nations people in your region. How did they use the environment to meet their needs before their encounters with European visitors and settlers? In the following activity, you will explore both the traditional and, if possible, the contemporary lifestyles of a First Nations group in your region.

A

**Beyond
Folklore**

**A.2**

*Following
the Paths to
the Future*

# CHARTING FUTURE PATHS

Research what is known about the origins and traditional lifestyles of First Nations peoples in your region. Then, if possible, research information about their contemporary (modern) lifestyles. Your library may contain little information on the subject; this is an ideal opportunity to interview people in the communities. There may be parents, relatives, or friends who could speak to your class.

Using texts, poems, and illustrations, create a mural about the lifestyle of First Nations peoples in your region. In teams or alone, choose one of the following aspects to represent in the mural:

–  the possible origins of First Nations groups in your region;

–  the climate and geography of the area;

–  the type of shelter used before and in use now;

–  the type of clothing worn long ago and today;

–  the food the people ate before and eat now;

–  the means of transportation long ago and today.

Remember that the environment played a major role in determining how traditional cultures met their needs. In designing your mural, demonstrate how the environment influenced the food, clothing, shelters, and transportation of the group you are studying.

Charting Future Paths, continued...

A
Beyond
Folklore

A.2
Following
the Paths to
the Future

Your research project involves several steps:

1. Review **Tools C4** and **E9** for help with the various stages in your research.

2. Review **Tools C8** and **D3** for help when you get to the editing and presentation stages.

3. In your writing, focus on the correct use of verbs in the present and the past tenses. Check your draft using **Tool C8**.

4. If possible, include a map of the world in your research presentation showing the route the First Nations peoples are believed to have taken to reach your region and other areas in which they settled. See **Tools D4** and **E10**. On your map, include contemporary political boundaries and traditional First Nations lands. Or alternatively, describe how these people tell the story of their first ancestors.

5. Present your research in the form of a mural illustrating the transition from past to present (and future, if you like). See **STEPSpage 28** and **Tool D3**. Look at how the illustrator complemented the different poems with his illustrations (see **pages 6** to **9** of *Discovering Culture and Values*). Can you use these ideas or adapt them in your mural?

6. On your research mural, you could add poems similar to the ones on **pages 6** to **9** in *Discovering Culture and Values*. See **Tools C3** and **E5**.

# E.2 TRADITIONAL AND CONTEMPORARY BEATS

Here is a list of topics you may want to explore for your mural on First Nations peoples.

**Important note:** Though your local museum may seem an unlikely source for information about modern life, it is an excellent starting point for your research. Museum curators often need to verify information about their artifacts with local groups. They may be able to give you names and contacts. At the very least, you should be able to obtain a list of other possible sources from your local museum. See **Tools A5** and **E9**. Be aware that many traditional songs, objects, and customs are intended for use during special ceremonies only. Also, music, art, and books that are mass-marketed are not always culturally authentic. The best examples of First Nations music, art, and customs are often available only from local groups.

### ART

– Wood, stone, or bone sculptures, carvings, or etchings: totems, canoes, masks, toys, path markers, burial markers, pictographs.

– Paintings and pigments: facial and body markings, decorative additions to tools and household items, ceremonial objects.

– Weaving, sewing, jewellery, clothing, ceremonial objects, decorative elements.
Many well-known artists of First Nations origin have become role models in the art world: Jackson Beardy, Roy Henry Vickers, Ashevak Kenojuak, Bill Reid, Daphne Odjig.

### LEISURE ACTIVITIES

Games, sports, story-telling, crafts (e.g., decorative additions to clothing, homes, utensils, tools).

In traditional Inuit culture, women often played a game where one woman makes a series of sounds which her partner then tries to repeat. The object of the game is to repeat the sounds without laughing. The woman who remains straight-faced the longest is the winner. Try this game with a partner! Can you keep a straight face longer than your partner?

Lacrosse is Canada's national sport. It is thought of as Canada's oldest organized sport, played by the Algonquin peoples of the St. Lawrence valley region.

A

Beyond
Folklore

A.2
*Following
the Paths to
the Future*

### RELIGIOUS OR SPIRITUAL BELIEFS AND CUSTOMS

Ceremonies for birth, adulthood, marriage, death, celebration, or mourning of important events. Medicines and remedies for ailments.

### GOVERNMENT

Roles of men and women. Rights of children. Decision-making process. Relationships with other cultural groups. What can you learn about recent developments in native land claims?

### MUSIC

Instruments, rhythms, tone of voice, ceremonial chants, lullabies, songs sung while working or playing.

For example, you could listen to samples of traditional and contemporary First Nations music to identify elements associated with pitch (high, low), tone (nasal, guttural, shrill, throaty, resounding) and duration (slow, quick). See **Tool B3**. To do this, you will need access to traditional and/or contemporary selections of First Nations music. Susan Aglukark, James Kim Bell, and Kashtin are examples of contemporary musicians and singers who are contributing to native culture and the Canadian music scene.

*Ojibway Drum*

A

Beyond
Folklore

A.2

*Following
the Paths to
the Future*

# E.3 GLOBAL WARMING: A DISASTER FOR THE NORTH!

Create a visual or audiovisual presentation to demonstrate how Inuit lifestyles would be affected by continued global warming.

**BACKGROUND INFORMATION**

For several years now, scientists believe that the temperature of the earth's surface has been rising. Summers are warmer. Humans burn great amounts of fossil fuels: coal, oil, natural gas. This produces carbon monoxide and carbon dioxide gases that build up in the atmosphere. These gases and other pollutants in the air prevent the sun's infrared rays reflected off of the earth's surface from leaving the atmosphere. Therefore, average temperatures are gradually increasing everywhere on Earth. This global warming trend has been called the "Greenhouse Effect".

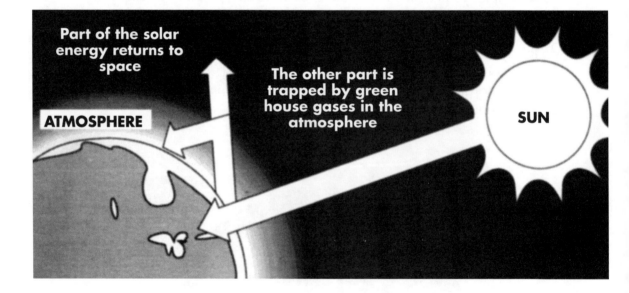

.3 GLOBAL WARMING: A DISASTER FOR THE NORTH!, continued...

**A**
Beyond
Folklore

**A.2**
*Following
the Paths to
the Future*

Imagine what would happen if the greenhouse effect were to cause the snow and ice at the polar caps to melt. The permafrost would thaw, turning the "frozen north" into a bog. Animals and people would have difficulty moving about. Houses would shift and settle into the ground. Ice would pile up on the land as it thawed and there would be extensive flooding as the water would sit on top of the ground rather than seeping into it.

These environmental changes would spell disaster for the Inuit. Use a poster, a mural, a comic strip, or a model to present your predictions on the following aspects of the damaging effects global warming would have on their lifestyles:

–  How would northern shelters be impacted?

–  How would means of transportation in the north be affected?

–  How would global warming affect the northern ecosystem? Consider the types of plants and animals present in the north. Would they be able to adapt to a different climate? Would they find their normal food sources and their shelters in a warmer climate?

Skim through **Tools D1** to **D10** to gather ideas and suggestions to help you prepare and evaluate your visual presentation.

A

Beyond

Folklore

**A.2**

*Following
the Paths to
the Future*

4 LANGUAGE CONTRIBUTIONS

Cultures, upon contact, often exchange words as easily as they exchange goods and experiences. If you look at a map of your area, you will most likely find places named by First Nations. Write them down and check different information sources (history books, *The Canadian Encyclopedia*, tourism agencies, Internet searches) to determine the origins and meanings of these names.

To start you off, here are a few names that were easy to locate in *The Canadian Encyclopedia* and other sources.

| | |
|---|---|
| **Canada** | *kanata*, Huron-Iroquois word meaning "village or settlement". |
| **Saskatchewan** | Cree word for "swift flowing river". |
| **Ontario** | native word meaning "beautiful lake" or "beautiful waters". |
| **Winnipeg** | *win-nipi*, Cree word for "murky waters". |
| **Antigonish** | *nategitkoonechk*, Micmac word meaning "where branches are torn off". |
| **Nanaimo** | *sneneymeuxw*, Coast Salish word meaning "great and mighty people". |
| **Inuvik** | Inuit word meaning "place of man". |

Native plant and animal names may also be a reflection of First Nations' contributions to your region (*kinnickinnick, bannock, wapiti, ookpik, caribou, pemmican*).

.4 LANGUAGE CONTRIBUTIONS, continued...

**A**
Beyond
Folklore

**A.2**
*Following
the Paths to
the Future*

Objects invented and used by First Nations people often kept their original names because the first Europeans arriving in Canada had no other word to describe them (*mukluks, umiak, moccasins, tipi, wigwam, amulet*). How would you explain them to someone from another country?

Obviously, many names of First Nations groups and famous leaders were derived from translations of the names by which these groups called themselves: Blackfoot (*Siksikaw* in the Algonquian language); Crowfoot (*Isapomuxika*, a famous Siksikaw chief). Other names, like *Inuit, Dene, Kutenai, Haida, Tlingit, Iroquois, Tsimshian, Ootek, Hiawatha*, were not translated.

Research the origin and significance of First Nations names for places, animals, plants, objects or the names of famous First Nations leaders, explorers, or women. Write a list of the words or names you wish to research. You might discover these names by browsing through an encyclopedia, or by talking with First Nations people, or by reading their legends or history books. Choose one or two names and report on the origin of the name, its meaning in the native language, and how this name was given to the person, place, or object. See **Tool C4**.

**To practise your pronunciation, create a rhythmic repetition using the names you researched.**

With a partner, choose two names from the list you created in the first part of this activity. Say them with rhythmic intonation. Repeat the words several times. Add movements and percussion (clapping, stomping, snapping fingers, etc.) to your rhythms.

Once you have two names, try adding others to form a rhythm where the first partner says the names and the second partner repeats the names using a different tone of voice.

See **Tool B3** to help you develop and evaluate this activity. **Tool E1** can help you with terms that you might be unfamiliar with.

# A
## Beyond Folklore

### A.3
### *Views on People and Nature*

Sc: Understand the relationships between living organisms and the environment.
FA: Use colour, shade, and shape to create symbolism, focus, or dominating effects.

Create a symbol to represent your vision of the environment and of our place in it. Your view may be similar to the ideas described below or it may be very different. See **STEPSpage 37** and **Tool D1**.

---

*Peter Knudtson and David Suzuki, in their book the **Wisdom of the Elders** (Toronto: Stoddart Publishing, Co., 1992), talk about common traits or themes in the native way of thinking. Here are some examples:*

- *a view of nature as a universe of something sacred, and full of life, that is always changing;*
- *"Spirit", however it is defined, is not seen as a single supreme being coming from one "right" religion;*
- *a view that people are a part of nature and were not placed on Earth to dominate or control nature;*
- *a view that people have been assigned the enormous responsibility of keeping harmony within the natural world and that they are not free to follow their own whims.*

---

What differences and/or similarities are there between these views and your own with respect to the environment?

LA: Identify/use information from appropriate sources to select pertinent details and to establish relationships.
FA: Experiment with a poster to represent interactions between living and non-living elements of the environment.

Read **pages 10** to **13** of **"A Treasured Heritage"** in *Discovering Culture and Values*. As you read, find the passages that talk about the environment and the grandfather's message to Jonathan. Write a summary of each. Using your notes, write the message that you think the chief was trying to pass on to his grandson. Use **Tool C1** to review and reflect on your interpretation.

- How does the chief feel that humans should act toward the environment?

- What messages in the story promote a respect for nature and for harmony?

- Do you think that Jonathan will act on his grandfather's message(s)? What actions could he take?

Create a poster to invite others to act on the message the chief was passing on to his grandson. See **Tools D1** and **D9**.

**A**

Beyond
Folklore

**A.3**
*Views on
People and
Nature*

**.1** LA: Identify/use selected information from appropriate sources to select pertinent details and to establish relationships. Experiment with a debate format to express a point of view, an opinion, an analysis.

Sc: Explore/study human activities and their impact on the ecosystem.

Are there environmental debates taking place in your area? Choose an ongoing environmental issue and decide which side of the argument you agree with. Prepare a debate or a speech to present your opinion, using **Tools B5** and **D1**.

**Or**

**.2** Sc: Explore/study human activities and their impact on the ecosystem.

SS: Understand that human activity involves satisfying basic needs and that it affects the environment.

FA: Experiment with a collage to represent interactions between living and non-living elements of the environment.

Represent the relationship between an ancient society and its environment in the form of a collage. See **Tools D1** and **D3** and **STEPSpage 38**.

**Or**

**.3** FA: Experiment with sculpting/modelling to represent plants/animals.

Create a clay model of an animal that you admire. See **STEPSpage 40** and **Tool D8**.

**Or**

**.4** FA: Experiment with dance to explore and envision possibilities for presenting ideas and movement. Use the space available with respect for the movements of others.

Create a dance telling the story of a forest that is threatened by a dark cloud. See **STEPSpage 42** and **Tools B3** and **D8**.

**Or**

.5 LA: Identify/use information from appropriate sources to select pertinent details and to establish relationships.

FA: Use colour, shade, and shape to create symbolism, focus, or dominating effects.

Examine the illustration on **page 10** of *Discovering Culture and Values*. Where does this story take place? How are the characters in the story dressed? How does the environment influence their choice of clothing?

On a blank paper divided into four sections, illustrate four environments different from the one shown on **page 10** of *Discovering Cultures and Values*. Include one or more people in each of your illustrations. Choose names for places and/or dwellings based on the environment or climate. As an example, how would you illustrate the environments for places named "Stony Plain" or "Rainbow Lake" or "Pine Point" or "Baie Verte"?

Analyze your illustrations using **Tool D1**.

SD: Understand the importance of change as a continual process in human development.

Answer the questions on **STEPSpages 43, 44** to explore the influences of human activity on the environment. Also, give examples of how we acknowledge changes from one stage to another in our lives. Use **Tools D1** and **D9** to review and reflect on how well you were able to complete the reflection questions and the above activity.

# SYMBOLS OF THE ENVIRONMENT

Create a symbol to represent your vision of the environment and of our place in it. Before you start, ask yourself these questions:

– What do plants and animals need in order to survive?

– Are there written symbols that are commonly used to represent elements of the environment?

Using **Tool D1**, examine the symbols below. These are just a few of the symbols used by North American First Nations to represent the basic needs of all living things:

**The Sun:** symbol of strength, warmth, life, rebirth

**Corn:** symbol for food

**Water:** symbol for the source of life, endurance, peace, and abundance or plenty

Look at the images on the drum to the right. This drum was made by an unknown artist of the Ojibway people. These people belong to the Cree nation. The artist used symbols to represent the unity between living things and their environment. Refer to the comments in **Tool D1**, and answer the following questions:

– What do you see in this image?

– What symbols were used to represent the sun, the water, living things, the earth?

– What geometrical shapes were used? What is the dominant geometrical shape? What does this shape represent?

Create your own symbols to show harmony between humans and the environment. Remember to include the basic needs in your symbols. Analyze your symbols using **Tool D1**.

**A**

Beyond
Folklore

**A.3**

*Views on
People and
Nature*

# E.2 PAST CIVILIZATIONS AND THEIR ENVIRONMENTS

Our cultural beliefs and values are reflected in our attitudes toward the environment and toward the other societies that live on Earth. In this planet's history, many civilizations have become extinct either because of their treatment of their environment or because they were ill-prepared to deal with invasions from other societies in search of more land. When a society can no longer support its members on the land available, the group must choose between controlling its numbers or expanding its living space. Often this expansion infringes on another society's territory.

Chose an ancient society that you know a little about. Using **Tool E8** and at least three other information sources, prepare a collection of words, illustrations, or symbols representing what you know about this society.

– How did this society interact with other societies and with the natural environment it inhabited?

– What impact did this society have on the natural plant and animal species in its environment?

– What are the positive and negative influences of this society?

– How can these influences be represented in the form of a collage?

Using **Tool D3**, arrange the ideas you have collected as a collage. Consider different shapes for presenting your ideas. For example, the pyramid is a shape often used to demonstrate dominance of one species over another. The web or the circle is often used to represent connections between species. How could these shapes add emphasis to your collage? If several students prepare collages, display them together as a mural.

| SOME OF TODAY'S OLDEST CULTURES | SOME ANCIENT CIVILIZATIONS OF THE PAST |
|---|---|
| Inuit (northern Canada) | Ancient Egyptian |
| Dene (northern Canada) | Sumerian (mid-east Asia) |
| Cree (Canadian plains) | Phoenician (mid-east Asia) |
| Haida (B.C., Canada, northwest coast) | Babylonian (mid-east Asia) |
| Salish (B.C., Canada) | Assyrian (mid-east Asia) |
| Iroquois (eastern Canada) | Viking (Scandinavian culture) |
| Micmac (eastern Canada) | Hun (Asian) |
| Mohawk (eastern Canada) | Beothuk (Newfoundland, Canada) |
| Penan (Sarawak, Malaysia) | Mycenaean (Ancient Greece) |
| Maori (New Zealand) | Celt (Ancient Great Britain) |
| Hopi (Arizona, USA) | Saxon (Germanic culture) |
| Yanomani (Brazil) | Aztec (Mexico) |
| Quechua (Peru)  Inca (Peru) | |
| Maya (Guatemala) | Ancient Roman |
| Aranda (Australia) | ... |
| San Bushmen (Southern Africa) | |
| !Kung (Botswana) | |
| Desano (Colombia) | |

A

Beyond Folklore

**A.3**

*Views on People and Nature*

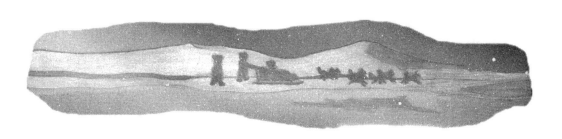

A

**Beyond
Folklore**

**A.3**

*Views on
People and
Nature*

# E.3 CREATE A CLAY MODEL OF AN ANIMAL YOU ADMIRE

You will need about 500 g of clay or modelling clay or dough, pointed sticks or objects for marking your clay, and a board or surface to work on. **Tool D8** has a recipe for making modelling dough.

Jonathan's grandfather offered Jonathan a feather to pass on the strength of the eagle. Among the animals you know, choose one that you admire. Think about what this animal means to you or what characteristic this animal represents for you. Design a sculpture of this animal using **Tool D8**.

1. With your hands, soften the clay by rolling it into balls or sausage-like rolls.

2. With your pointed sticks or other objects, experiment with marking different textures in the clay. Try to represent feathers, fur, scales, etc.

3. Make several different pieces and experiment with ways to attach them together. Making sure your pieces are firmly pinched together is especially important if you are using clay that will be fired (baked) in a kiln.

4. Now you are ready to start working on your animal. Imagine how you would like to present your animal. You might want to look at pictures or draw a sketch of your animal before you start.

5. Roll your clay into a ball. Using as much of the clay as possible, divide the clay into balls or rolls to form the basic structure of your animal. Shape the balls or rolls before connecting them together. Then use your pointed sticks or other objects to add the final details.

6. When you are finished modelling your clay, write an explanation about why you chose this animal and what it represents to you. Check your spelling and your punctuation. Then copy this text onto an index card to be placed beside your finished model. Take a picture of your sculpture to add to your *Thoughtsteps Journal*.

In your culture, or in your geographical region, do some animals have symbolic value? Think of stories you know about bear, deer, mice, wolves, bison, coyotes, salmon, crows, and other animals. How are these animals portrayed? What human qualities do we associate with these animals?

# E.4 TELL A STORY IN DANCE

Here is the start of a story that you might use for your choreography:

> *One day, the inhabitants of the forest watched in horror as an ominous black cloud filled the horizon. As the cloud drew closer, the sky became completely black. The forest dwellers had no idea what it was and they were extremely afraid...*

With a group, finish the story on a positive note. To do this, you will need to think of what powerful actions the citizens of the forest will decide to take. Decide how you might tell the story in the form of a dance. See **Tools B3** and **D8**. **Extension E.6** from activity path **A.1 Needs and Environment** also offers suggestions for preparing your dance.

Here are some ideas to get you started:

– How will you show the dark cloud advancing? How was it made?

– How will you represent the forest creatures? What will happen to them? How do they feel?

– What will happen to their sources of food, water, shelter, and air?

– How will you challenge and overcome this danger?

– Will you use special effects in your choreography?

Present your dance to your classmates. See **Tools B3** and **D8**. Tape the dance on video if you would like to see it again. See **Tool D10**.

A DISCUSSION ON SOCIETIES

With a group, discuss the questions below to explore the influences of human activity on the environment.

1. How does one society meet its needs without destroying the needs of other species or of other societies?

2. What has happened to past societies who have not been able to meet their needs within their own environments? Name a society which migrated to another region. Name a society which went to war with neighbouring societies. Name a society which disappeared because it was overpowered by another society. Can you think of other solutions? What has happened to the societies you named?

3. What effect does resource depletion (deforestation, mining, over-fishing, intense agriculture) have on the water, the land, the air, and the food that human societies, animals, and plants need to survive? Think of examples of societies where resource depletion was the reason for their downfall.

4. What effect does pollution have on the water, the land, the air, and the food that human societies, animals, and plants need to survive? Think of examples of societies where pollution was the reason for a decrease in population or for their downfall.

5. Pollution and resource depletion are problems created by humans as they struggle to meet their expanding needs. What actions are people taking to improve the ways that we meet our needs so that we don't pollute and destroy our environment? What actions have you taken in the past to minimize the destructive forces of pollution or of resource depletion?

**A**

**Beyond Folklore**

**A.3**

*Views on People and Nature*

**With a group, discuss the questions below to explore the influences of traditions on members of a cultural group.**

1. How did Jonathan's grandfather acknowledge that Jonathan was no longer a little boy at the end of the story **"A Treasured Heritage"** on **page 13** of *Discovering Culture and Values*? Would this gesture have the same meaning in your family? If not, can you identify a gesture that would have a similar meaning for you?

2. By his gesture of giving the feather to Jonathan, is the chief handing over certain responsibilities to his grandson? What might they be? Review the messages the chief talked about. When does the society you live in recognize children as adults? What rights and privileges are given to adults that are not available to children in our society? What responsibilities come with the right to be called an adult?

3. You have probably heard the phrase, *You're too young to...* It usually implies that you're not big enough, responsible enough, strong enough, wise enough, or old enough to do something. Describe one event from your past where an adult used a similar expression with you (or with someone you know). Are you old enough now or do you still have to wait? How will you know when you are old enough?

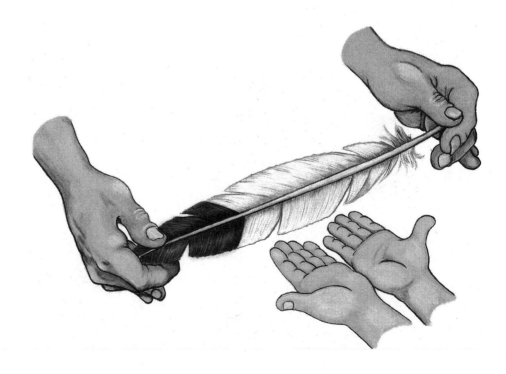

LA: Identify/use information from images to select pertinent details and to establish relationships.

FA: Express an opinion about art by identifying the elements used to create art: technique, medium, juxtaposition of elements and their location in space. Use colour, shade, and shape to create symbolism and equilibrium.

In the painting shown on **page 14** of *Discovering Culture and Values*, identify the colours, the shapes, and the symbols that Jackson Beardy uses. Use **Tool D1** to help you with your appreciation of this painting. Beardy is presenting his perception of interdependence and harmony between the environment and living organisms.

- How does the circle add to Beardy's art? What other geometric shapes are used? What do they represent?

- Which animal is represented?

- What is happening in the image?

- What are the dominant colours? How do they make you feel?

- What symbols and colours are used to represent water, air, life, unity, earth and the sun?

**Beardy believes colours can convey specific emotions, places, or events. Here is his classification of colours:**
- **blue:** purity, loyalty, water (a colour of the South)
- **red:** bravery, anger, blood, courage, wealth, love, beauty (a colour of the East)
- **yellow:** warmth, love, bravery (a colour of the West)
- **green:** growth, spirituality, eternity
- **black:** strength, death, night, endurance
- **brown:** earth, soil, strength, openness, warmth, relaxation
- **orange:** fire, pride, dusk
- **white:** purity, sacredness, birth (a colour of the North)

LA: Identify/use information from images to select pertinent details and to establish relationships.

FA: Create a collage using colour, shade, and shape to create symbolism and equilibrium.

Using **Tools D1** and **D3**, create a circular collage illustrating how humans are dependent on their environment. Using symbolic colours similar to Beardy's (described above), choose colours that have meaning for you and select the elements that you want to present: air, water, earth, life, etc. The circular background is used to symbolize unity and life.

**.1** SS: Understand how humans attempt, through symbolism, and the expression of their values,
to make sense of, or control, their environment.
FA: Use colour, shade, shape to create symbolism and equilibrium.

What other symbols in your society or your culture are recognized by a large
number of people? Using **Tools D1** and **D3**, represent them on a collage titled
"Symbols Worth a Thousand Words". The Ukrainian *pysanka*, or painted Easter
egg, uses many different visual symbols. Chinese letters are also an excellent
example of symbols with meanings. Street signs, company or team logos, and
national flags are symbols that people recognize at a glance.

To explore a few of the graphic symbols that are used by First Nations in their
art, see **STEPSpage 48**.

**Or**

**.2** LA: Identify/use appropriate sources of information to reproduce or recall details.
SS: Understand how humans attempt, through symbolism and the expression of their values, to
make sense of, or control, their environment.

Write a poem about your views on the circle of life. Include ideas about what
you most value about life and its different stages. Think of how you can incorporate birth, childhood, adulthood, growing, aging, and dying into your poem.
You might choose to add the poem to your collage. See **Tools C3** and **E5** for
ideas.

**Or**

**.3** SS: Understand how humans attempt, through symbolism and the expression of their values, to
make sense of, or control, their environment.
FA: Use colour, shade, shape to create symbolism and equilibrium.

In some cultures, colours carry symbolic meanings. In others, little importance is
attached to the symbolism of colours. To test the significance of colours among
your peers, prepare a survey matrix (see **Tool A3**) using Beardy's colours and
classifications. List the colours along one axis and the different symbols and
characteristics along the other. Leave enough room on your matrix to include
other suggestions from your survey group. Survey a group of 25 people. Ask
each person to match the colours with the meanings listed. Compare their
answers to Beardy's classification.

– Are there similarities in the answers from the survey group and in Beardy's classification?

– Are some answers more common than others?

– In your survey, were the participants able to see the answers given by others? If so, did this influence their answers? If not, how did you prepare your survey to avoid bias in the answers?

 SD: Recognize, examine, and appreciate individual/group differences in point of view and opinions.

Evaluate the techniques and symbols you used in creating your collage using **Tools D1** and **D3**. In your comments about your collage, explain the symbolism of the shapes and colours you used.

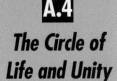

## A
### Beyond
### Folklore

## A.4
### The Circle of
### Life and Unity

.1 SYMBOLISM IN NATIVE ART

Examine works by different native artists to explore the graphic symbols used by First Nations in their art. In First Nations art, symbols are often used to represent different aspects of life and the environment. The symbols of the sun and water are very important. They are found everywhere, in pottery, in sculptures, in illustrations. Can you find other symbols that you recognize in First Nations art from your or other regions? See **Tool D1**. In your *Thoughtsteps Journal*, illustrate these symbols and provide an explanation for each one.

## The Sun

The sun is the symbol of life, of warmth, of rebirth of all life on Earth. Here are some ways in which different First Nations peoples represent the sun in their culture:

 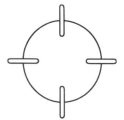  

From Barbra L. Wardle, *Native American Symbolism in the Classroom*, Art Education, September 1990.

## Water

The symbol of water is used to represent all forms of life, endurance, peace, purity, abundance, and survival.

From Barbra L. Wardle, *Native American Symbolism in the Classroom*, Art Education, September 1990.

What other graphic symbols can you find in the art of the First Nations in your area? What symbols do they use to represent:

- plants, trees, berries, etc.;
- lightning, storms, wind, rain;
- food;
- animals;
- shelter;
- actions?

LA: Identify/use information from ideas to establish relationships and question the premises for them.

FA: Express an opinion, an emotion, or a sentiment regarding a work of art. Explore the similarities or differences between human traits and environmental objects.

Masks have long been used to represent animals, plants, elements of nature, mythical creatures, and more. **Pages 15** to **17** of *Discovering Culture and Values* show three different types of masks. Answer the questions on **STEPSpage 52** as you examine these masks. See **Tool D1**.

 LA: Identify/use information from ideas to establish relationships and question the premises for them. Demonstrate an understanding of language conventions.

Sc: Understand the relationships between living organisms and the environment.

SS: Understand that human activity affects the environment.

FA: Experiment with dialogue in a skit to explore social interactions. In a positive manner, support the roles played by others. Experiment with sculpting to create imaginary characters/legendary heroes.

In this activity, you will construct a mask representing an element of your environment, then present it in a short skit.

Before constructing your mask, choose a partner and improvise a short dialogue (a short conversation) on one of the questions below. See **Tool B2**. Your improvisation doesn't need a lot of preparation. This exercise should only take 10 to 15 minutes. You might want to videotape your improvisation. See **Tool D10**.

– If trees could talk, what would they whisper to us?

– If the sun could speak, what would it have to tell us?

– If the river could babble with words, what would it say?

– If we could speak to the animals in their language, what would we ask them?

– If the earth could talk, what questions might we ask it?

For different ideas on constructing your masks, see **STEPSpages 53** to **55**.

Then choose a team of six people (or fewer, if you want to play more than one role). Together, write a dialogue for a short play where an animal, a tree, the earth, a person, a stream and the sun meet in the forest, by the edge of a lake to talk about their ideas on the state of the environment and their feelings towards nature.

A

Beyond
Folklore

**A.5**

*The Message
Behind
the Mask*

What might they say to each other? What would they like to change? Why? Are they satisfied with their surroundings? What problems might they discuss? What solutions might they propose?

See **Tool C8** to refine your dialogue. Focus on using the correct punctuation for a script. Usually the actors' names are written in capital letters followed by a colon and then the dialogue (e.g., SPEAKER: written dialogue). See **Tools B2** and **B3** for hints on speaking and presenting to an audience. In presenting your short play or skit, will you have music? lighting? costumes? background decor? mime? dancing? **Tool D8** contains ideas on how to prepare props for your presentation.

**.1** LA: Improvise a dialogue or visual representation to express a point of view, an opinion, an emotion, or an analysis.

Invent a mime, a dance, or a short explanation to demonstrate the symbolic meaning of your mask. See **Tools B2** and **D8**.

**Or**

**.2** LA: Improvise a dialogue or visual representation to express a point of view, an opinion, an emotion, or an analysis.
FA: Use the space available according to intent of actions.

Organize a parade to present your masks to others in your school. The parade could be the opening scene of your play. See **Tools B2** and **D8**. Each actor could describe the character of his or her mask.

**Or**

**.3** LA: Identify/use information from images to establish relationships and question the premises for them.
FA: Use colour, shade, and shape to create symbolism.

Using a variety of information sources (museums, art galleries, history books, references on cultural groups or ancient civilizations), prepare a series of illustrations of masks from different cultures. For each mask illustrated, write a brief description. Include information on the characteristics of the mask and how they give meaning to the mask. Explain also which cultural group or artist designed the mask.

SD: Recognize, examine, and appreciate individual/group differences in points of view, opinions, and values.

Comment on your presentation and the masks you created, using **Tools B2, B3**, and **D1**. In this activity, you used masks to represent elements of nature. In your culture, are there ceremonies or events where masks are used? If so, what do these masks represent?

MASK EXPLORERS

Choose one of the masks on **pages 15** to **17** of *Discovering Culture and Values*. Complete the following details about the mask.

Name of the mask: _____

Of the three masks, this is the mask that I prefer because _____

_____.

When I look at this mask, I feel _____

because _____.

The shapes that I see in this mask are: _____

_____.

I think that these shapes represent _____

_____.

If this mask represented a human being, I think the person would be _____

_____.

(Describe the personality of the mask as though it were a person.)

The colours used in this mask are: _____.

I think they represent _____.

To make this mask, the artist used the following materials: _____.

I think that the artist made this mask using the technique called _____

_____ (name the technique).

This technique involves the following steps:

• _____

• _____

• _____

• _____

# MASK MAKERS

In order to give lifelike qualities to the characters in your play, prepare masks representing them. **Pages 15** to **17** of *Discovering Culture and Values* show three different types of masks. Decorate your mask with symbols that represent the qualities of the character.

Here are a few techniques to use in constructing the base for your mask. See **Tool D8** to establish the criteria for evaluating your masks.

**TECHNIQUE:** sculpting/shaping

**MATERIALS REQUIRED:**     cardboard or bristol board
construction paper of different colours
glue, scissors

### THE BASE STRUCTURE:

1. Cut two or four slits into a piece of cardboard or construction paper.

2. Fold the sides one over the other to give a curved shape to your mask. You can modify the shape to suit your needs before you glue it together.

3. Decide which way you want your mask to fit. Hold the mask over your face and use a pencil to mark where the holes need to be for you to see out. Remove the mask and cut out the openings for your eyes.

   You can, for example, wear the mask on top of your head like Art Thompson's wolf mask on **page 15** of *Discovering Culture and Values*.

4. Another shaping technique is to draw a circle in the cardboard. Cut out the openings for your eyes. Cut a slit in the base of the circle and overlap the two sides to form a cone. Glue the cone shape together. Add a paper or elastic strap to hold the mask to your face.

5. You could also use a shoe box or other box as the base and add other materials to it. For other ideas, see **Tool D8**. The next step is to transform your base into a mask representing a character such as an animal or mythical being.

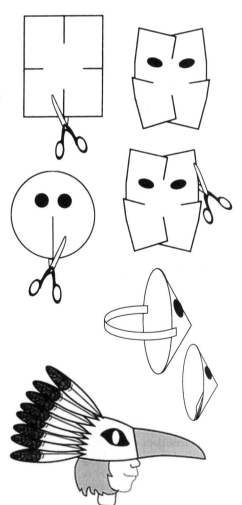

**A**

Beyond
Folklore

**A.5**

*The Message
Behind
the Mask*

 **MASK MAKERS,** continued...

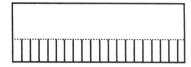

1. Fold a piece of paper as shown. Cut strips into the paper up to the fold line. Curve the paper to form a cylinder or a cone. The strips will allow you to glue the shape to your mask. These shapes can be used to make ears, noses, beaks, the sun's rays, etc.

2. Cut out other shapes for feathers, manes, fur. Use your scissors to curl the strips or fold them to give them shape.

3. Use your imagination. All kinds of materials can be used to add colour and creativity to your mask: cloth, raffia, wool, twigs, grasses, feathers, etc.

For more ideas, refer to **Tool D8**.

**MASK MAKERS,** continued...

*Mask construction using symmetry and pastels or chalk:*

1. Observe the masks on **pages 16** and **17** of *Discovering Culture and Values*. These masks have very few colours and are symmetrical.

2. Choose an emotion, a quality or a personality that you would like to represent with your mask.

3. Choose a maximum of four colours, according to what you would like to represent. See **STEPSpage 45** for one artist's description of colours. You could test your colours on a piece of paper before you start painting or colouring your mask.

4. Draw your mask using as much of your paper as possible. Concentrate on the symmetry of your mask. For example, if you draw a triangle on the left side, then draw one in the same location on the right side of the mask.

5. In drawing your mask, you might choose to use repetitive motifs:

or textures:

6. Once you have finished your mask, glue it onto a piece of bristol board. Cut out the contour of your mask. Decorate it with strips of wool, paper, twigs, etc. Attach a string to each side of the mask so you can wear it over your face.

7. Either cut out openings in your mask to make eyes or wear the mask on top of your head.

Preparing your *Thoughtsteps Journal*

# B

# Beautiful Noise

 Open your *Thoughtsteps Journal*. Add to it a blank page, a lined page, and two more blank pages.
- On the first page, write the title of your theme.
- On the lined page, write the words "Table of Contents". As you work through the theme, list your activities here.
- On the next blank page, list your ideas, words, knowledge relating to your country's cultural heritage, music, traditions, language, and contributions, etc. See **Tool A2**.

 Using your list of ideas from the brainstorming activity, make a poster on the next page of your *Thoughtsteps Journal*. Show words and images about the theme *Discovering Culture and Values:* **Beautiful Noise**.

On the back of this page, write the title "Discovering New Words". As you work through the activities in this theme, list on this page any new words you encounter.

**E.1** Use a dictionary to review spelling.

**Or**

**E.2** Create a class poster combining everyone's ideas.

**Or**

**E.3** Look through other resource books for ideas for illustrations or words. Add them to your poster.

**Or**

**E.4** Add illustrations to your title page.

**Or**

**E.5** Add a **Bibliography** page. See **Tool A5** to learn how to list your sources.

**R** Check your poster for spelling: remember it's a tool you will use during the entire theme! Does it represent the theme? At the bottom of the poster, write down three ideas you would like to explore in this theme.

LA: Identify/use information from a text or image to infer, imagine, and extrapolate.
SS: Understand that human activity affects the environment. Study a milieu to identify and compare human and physical traits present.
FA: Experiment with drawings to represent mental images of certain facets of the environment.

Imagine what your area would have been like when people first began living in North America. Look out the window. What would you need to remove (buildings, plants, people) to return the area to its natural state before humans lived there? Sketch the landscape the first settlers would have seen when they arrived in your area. How might you have reacted if you were the first to discover and settle in this place?

On a separate piece of paper, sketch your house and other changes you would make to this area. Cut out these images and glue them on your original sketch.

Now imagine that many other groups have also discovered your area. Would you be happy or disappointed to see that these people also wanted to live in your area? To answer this question, think about the feelings you experience when people move into your school or your neighbourhood. Do you feel excited, curious, nervous? Do you ever wonder how the newcomers might feel?

As a group, combine your illustrations to make a mural of your area. Consult **Tools D1** and **E9** to discuss your sketches and the changes your group has proposed for this area.

What might your area be like 100 years from now? Describe the changes that might take place.

LA: Identify/use information from images to select pertinent details and establish relationships.
SS: Study a milieu to identify and compare human and physical traits present. Understand how humans attempt to make sense of their environment through the study of elements of their past and through interaction with other cultures.
FA: Experiment with sculpting and modelling techniques to represent certain facets of the environment. Identify the elements used to create art: juxtaposition of elements and location in space.

Read the text **"Did You Know That..."** on **page 19** of *Discovering Culture and Values*. Using **Tools D1** and **E9**, observe and analyze the reproductions by Paul Kane, William Raphaël, Jean Palardy, and Miyuki Tanobe on **pages 20** to **23** of *Discovering Culture and Values*. Discuss the four reproductions by answering the questions on **STEPSpages 60 and 61**.

After observing the reproductions, create a three-dimensional model to depict a scene from the history of Canadian immigrants. Write an explanation of your model describing the movement, sounds, and emotions in your scene. See **STEPSpages 62, 63** for directions on creating your model and **Tool D8** for the criteria with which to evaluate it.

**.1** LA: Identify/use information from text and images to describe characteristics.
SS: Study a milieu to identify and compare human and physical traits present. Understand how humans attempt to make sense of their environment through the study of elements of their past and through interaction with other cultures.

Early settlers often kept a journal and included in it sketches of what they saw. With the invention of photography, people began to keep scrapbooks containing photos of their life experiences. Were it not for these early historians, we would have few written or visual records of the past.

Years from now, your school projects and activities will be forgotten. So that you can keep a record of the model you created, take pictures of it from different angles. Glue the pictures and your written description into your *Thoughtsteps Journal*. See **Tools D1** and **E9** for questions to consider in arranging your work.

**Or**

**.2** LA: Identify/use information from text and images to describe characteristics.
SS: Study a milieu to identify and compare human and physical traits present. Understand how humans attempt to make sense of their environment through the study of elements of their past and through interaction with other cultures.

Another form of historical record-keeping became possible with the invention of the video camera. Historical events, archeological sites, memorable ceremonies are now often preserved on videotape. To preserve your model and the information you gathered, videotape your model while you narrate your description of it. If possible, include sound effects to make the model seem more realistic. If you have miniature figurines in your model, consider how you might manipulate them in different shots to depict movement. You could use magnets underneath the model or tape the figurines to bamboo sticks or attach strings. You could also use the pause button to enable you to move the figurines between shots. For other ideas, see **Tools D1** and **D10**.

**Or**

**.3** LA: Identify/use information from text and images to describe characteristics.
SS: Study a milieu to identify and compare human and physical traits present. Understand how humans attempt to make sense of their environment through the study of elements of their past and through interaction with other cultures.

Using what you learned by creating your scene of the past, prepare a three-dimensional model to depict a scene representing your region in the future. Include a written or taped explanation of your model. Again, think about ways that you might represent movement, sounds, emotions. Review **STEPS pages 62, 63** for directions on creating your model and **Tools D1** and **D8** for the criteria with which to evaluate it.

Or

 **.4** LA: Identify/use information from text/images to select pertinent details and establish relationships.
SS: Study a milieu to identify and compare human and physical traits present. Understand how humans attempt to make sense of their environment through the study of elements of their past and through interaction with other cultures.

Some early settlers wrote autobiographies about their adventures. Others had their tales recorded by children, grandchildren, or friends. Ask an elderly person in your neighbourhood or in your family to share their favourite story with you. Record it on tape and then write it as a story. See **Tools C4** and **C8**.

 SD: Identify, develop, and sustain means of improving relationships and interactions with others.

Evaluate your model (or models) by answering the following questions:

1. Does your scene contain only elements from the time period which it depicts?

2. How does your scene represent the season that you chose to depict?

3. How does your scene make use of different colours, textures, and shapes?

4. In what ways are you satisfied with your model? What elements would you change if you were to make another model?

5. What did you learn about the lifestyles of the first settlers in North America by observing the paintings and by designing your model?

6. How well did your group work together to create this model? How could you have improved your working relationship?

Include your answers in your *Thoughtsteps Journal*. Complete the evaluation forms from **Tools D1** and **D8** as well.

# EXPLORING IMAGES FOR CLUES TO THE PAST

Observe the painting **"Blackfoot Chief and Subordinates"**, by Paul Kane on **page 20** of *Discovering Culture and Values*. Describe what you see by answering the following questions and the questions from **Tool D1**. Record your answers in your *Thoughtsteps Journal*.

– Observe the headdresses and the clothes. What materials were used to make them?

– What differences are there in the costumes? Describe them.

– What do you see in the background?

– What does the sky look like? Do you think the artist wanted to represent a calm atmosphere or a stormy one? What is the mood of the painting?

– In the painting, the clouds appear to be moving away from the scene. What could this movement symbolize in the relationships between the people depicted? Why?

– What do you like or dislike about this painting? Explain.

– What aspects of these people's lives can you not gather information about simply by observing this painting? Where could you go to find this missing information?

# EXPLORING IMAGES FOR CLUES TO THE PAST, continued...

Now observe the reproductions **"Behind the Bonsecours Market, Montreal"**, **"Potato Picking"**, and **"Monday, Washing Day"** on **pages 21** to **23** of **Discovering Culture and Values**. Describe what you see by answering the following questions and those from **Tools D1** and **E9**. Again, record your answers in your **Thoughtsteps Journal**.

– Describe at least five different activities that are taking place in each of these paintings.

– What elements strike you in each of these paintings? Explain.

– Do these paintings tell you something you didn't know about how or why immigrants came to this country? Explain your answer.

– What questions do you have about the people's lifestyles that these paintings are unable to answer for you? Who could you ask or where could you find the answers to your questions?

# DEPICTING SCENES FROM THE PAST

Create a three-dimensional model to depict a scene from the lives of the early settlers. Display a written explanation of your model beside it.

## Getting organized

Examine the paintings on **pages 20** to **23** of *Discovering Culture and Values* and the questions on **STEPSpage 60**. These will help you generate ideas for your model. See **Tool D8** to review the criteria for evaluating your model. Work with other students if you wish. Before you start building your model, you will need to make some decisions.

– What is the mood of your scene: peaceful, working, at war, teaching, or…?

– What season is it and how can the weather be used to accent the mood of your model?

– Who are the characters in your scene? How are they dressed? What actions are they engaged in? What are their facial expressions?

– What other elements do you need to add to your model (animals, vegetation, buildings, transportation methods, tools, etc.)?

– What information do you need to research for the model or for the text that will accompany your model? Examine more than one source of information.

If you are working as a group, you can work together on the research or assign one category to each person: food, clothing, shelter, work and roles in the community, activities for pleasure, and so on. See **Tools A6** and **A7** for ideas on how to divide tasks for your project.

## Creating the model

1. Decide on a base for your model. Cover it with crumpled brown, green, or white paper. Add texture to the landscape by using sand, pebbles, twigs, plasticine, etc.

2. Use plasticine or modelling clay to shape your people and the elements of the village or community. Remember to include everything you discussed in your planning stage: actions, clothing, expressions, etc. You might add feathers or beads to the clothing. The clothing and structures (tipis, canoes, etc.) could be made from paper, cut out, and coloured with different motifs. See **Tool D8** for suggestions and an evaluation form for your sculpture.

## Creating the text

Remember that your text is used to give additional information about the scene you have created. Avoid writing about things that are already visible in the scene. Write only details which cannot be represented visually (conversations, smells, reasons for certain activities, etc.). Once you have written your draft version, see **Tool C8** and edit your work before you write the final version.

B

Beautiful
Noise

**B.2**

*From Place
to Place by
Land or Sea*

LA: Identify/use information from a text/image to predict, infer, imagine, and extrapolate. Organize selected information logically and creatively to express a point of view.

SS: Understand how humans attempt to make sense of their environment by studying elements of their past and attempting to predict future elements or events.

SD: Recognize, examine, and appreciate individual/group differences in ability to take initiative and in means of attaining a goal.

If you are not of First Nations descent, your ancestors would probably have immigrated to North America within the past 400 years. If you are of First Nations descent, your ancestors may have arrived in this land thousands of years ago.

Your task is to write a short description of how your ancestors might have felt when they arrived in this land. To help you with your description, observe the paintings on **pages 20** to **23** of *Discovering Culture and Values* and read the poem **"Discovering Freedom"** on **page 24**. The paintings reflect different periods in Canada's history: First Nations, early European settlement in the eastern provinces, agricultural settlements across the country, and modern urban settings. The poem **"Discovering Freedom"** describes the hopes of people who move to another land. See **STEPSpage 67** and **Tool D1** for a list of questions to help you gather ideas for your description.

LA: Identify/use information from an image to predict, infer, imagine, and extrapolate. Organize selected information logically and creatively to express a point of view. Demonstrate an understanding of language conventions.

SS: Understand how humans attempt to make sense of their environment by studying elements of their past and attempting to predict future elements or events.

FA: Experiment with illustrations using colour, shade, and shape to create depth, texture, perspective, and focus.

Imagine that you are one of your ancestors arriving in this land from another country. In your *Thoughtsteps Journal*, write one or more diary entries about your voyage, what emotions you experienced during your travels, and how you felt when you finally arrived in North America. Consult at least three different sources of information to gather details about the time period you are describing. These sources may include information from your parents or grandparents or from historical texts or images from your local museum and so on.

If you have recently immigrated to this country, then you won't have to imagine anything! Write about your real journey and your real emotions.

In your description, include the sounds, sights, and smells of your new "homeland". See **Tool D1** to help you organize your description. Use **Tools C8** and **E2** to check your work before writing the final copy. Even though this event takes place in the past, remember that you are writing about it as though you were there. Check that your descriptions are written in the present tense. Include an illustration of your journey. Begin by drawing only yourself and your means of transportation. These are to be the dominant elements in your picture. Use felt pens to colour them. Then colour in the background using pastels. Be certain that the background complements your illustrations of yourself, your means of transportation, and your emotions. Rub the pastels with a paper towel to give your background a faded appearance. Use **Tool D1** to establish your criteria for evaluation.

**E.1** SS: Organize a series of events on a timeline.
   FA: Formulate a monologue from a given theme. Use appropriate gestures, voice, and special effects.

Using your illustration and your journal, prepare a short skit to represent all or part of your imaginary journey. Think about how to add expression and rhythm to your skit. See **Tools B2** and **D1**.

If this was a group activity, organize the order of your presentations in a chronological timeline. See **Tool D8**.

## Or

**E.2** LA: Demonstrate an understanding of language conventions.

To explore how to change a written text from the present tense to the past tense, rewrite a section of your journal entry as though you were describing this event to one of your grandchildren many years later. See **Tools C8** and **E2**.

## Or

.3 LA: Identify/use information from appropriate sources to analyze characteristics and to establish relationships.
   SS: Understand that human activity is related to economics.
   FA: Formulate a dialogue from a given theme. Use gestures, voice, and special effects. In a positive manner, support the roles played by others.

If one of your parents were transferred to a job in another country, how would you feel about moving away from your friends and relatives here? Tell your imaginary situation to a friend. Explain why you are leaving, where you are moving, and what you propose to bring with you to remind you of home. In your simulation, your friend's role is to react to your explanation. If you are happy or sad about the move, how does your friend feel? What can your friend say or do to express his or her feelings? See **Tools B2** and **D1** for preparation suggestions. Together with your friend, present your dialogue as a skit to your classmates. If you decide to videotape your interview, consult **Tool D10**.

In your skit, you may wish to prepare an actual suitcase filled with objects, to show your friend the items you have chosen to put in your luggage. See extension activity **E.4**.

## B
## Beautiful Noise

### B.2
### *From Place to Place by Land or Sea*

Comment on how you felt during the interview as you imagined yourself leaving your friend and your country.

**Or**

**.4** LA: Identify/use information from appropriate sources to analyze characteristics and establish relationships.
FA: Identify the elements used to create art through juxtaposition of elements in a collage.

Create a collage or sculpture, or arrange items in a real trunk, to show what one of the first immigrants might have brought to Canada. Include a text that explains your choices. **Tools D1**, **D3**, and/or **D8** contain ideas and general evaluation forms to use for this activity. See **STEPSpages 68, 69** for background information.

**Or**

**.5** LA: Identify/use information from appropriate sources to analyze characteristics and establish relationships. Experiment with interviews as a means of expressing a point of view, an opinion.

Interview a recent Canadian immigrant. Before conducting your interview, prepare a series of questions to find out:

– Why did the person come to Canada?

– Why did this person choose Canada instead of another country?

– Were there problems in this person's homeland (famine, disease, inequities)?

– What is this person's dream for the new land?

– What does this person intend to do or already do for work?

– What positive or negative personal experiences could this person share with you?

For information on writing open-ended questions for your interviews, see **Tool A4**. **Tool B4** offers suggestions for preparing and evaluating your interview.

SD: Identify, develop, and sustain means of improving expression and effective communication, relationships, and interactions with others.

Use **Tools C1** and **C8** to evaluate your descriptions and **Tool D1** to analyze your illustration.

– Comment on three qualities of your illustration and your text.

– What factors affected your choice of means of transportation?

– Can you now imagine how your ancestors might have felt when they first arrived in North America?

– How do you think new immigrants feel when they arrive in their new country?

HOW WOULD YOU HAVE FELT?

Observe the paintings by Paul Kane, William Raphaël, Jean Palardy, and Miyuki Tanobe on **pages 20** to **23** of *Discovering Culture and Values*. Then read the poem **"Discovering Freedom"** on **page 24**.

Answer the following questions, as well as those from **Tool D1**, to help you gather ideas for writing your description of how your ancestors (or how you) felt when they (you) arrived in this land. You may wish to consult other information sources or resource people to help you with these answers and your description.

1. How do you think the first settlers or immigrants in these paintings felt when they first arrived in this land? Do you think these people were surprised or worried? Did they feel appreciated or threatened?

2. Were they greeted warmly or ignored?

3. What did they see when they first arrived?

4. What noises might they have heard? What odours could they have smelled?

5. If you were emigrating to a new country, would you have thoughts like those of the person who wrote this poem?

6. Would you like to emigrate (move away) to another country? Why?

7. Have you ever moved to another place or to another country? If so, what was your reaction? How were you received? What emotions did you experience?

8. Brainstorm a list of reasons why a person would leave his or her homeland and move to another place. You may get ideas for this list simply by asking your classmates why their ancestors, or why they, moved to your area. From your list, choose one of the reasons and incorporate it into your description of your thoughts and emotions.

B

**Beautiful
Noise**

**B.2**

*From Place
to Place by
Land or Sea*

# E.4 WHAT SHOULD I PACK?

Create a collage or a sculpture, or pack a real trunk to show what one of the first immigrants to Canada might have brought with them. Imagine that you are immigrating to the New World. You're excited about playing a role in building the colonies that will later become Canada. Decide whether you want to be a woodcutter, a teacher, an explorer, a nursing sister, a prospector, a laundry worker, a farmer, a fisherman, a shop-keeper, a trader, or some other role. Consult several different sources of information to find out what materials or clothes you would have needed at that time to do the job.

Prepare your trunk for the journey to the New World. Include in it a text explaining your choices for the contents. See **Tool D3** if you are going to make a collage or **Tool D8** if you plan to make a sculpture.

B

Beautiful
Noise

B.2

*From Place
to Place by
Land or Sea*

*Starting out*

*The people who built Canada to what it is today came from many parts of the world. Long before the first Europeans arrived, the First Nations peoples were well established in both North and South America. Then, over 500 years ago, Europeans came and called this land the "New World". It was a world to explore, to exploit, to discover.*

*For some of the first immigrants, Canada was a place of adventure and opportunity. For others, it was a refuge from sickness or imprisonment in their homeland. Most of the new immigrants saw Canada as a place where they would have the chance to start a new life.*

*The journey to get here was long and exhausting. There was no question of returning quickly to the homeland. The people who came here came to stay for months or years or even for the rest of their lives. Knowing that they would be in Canada for a long time, they often brought keepsakes to remind them of the country they had left. But their suitcases and trunks couldn't hold everything that they wanted to bring with them. They had to make some difficult choices.*

*If you were one of these early immigrants moving to Canada, what would you bring with you to remind you of your past? Decide first which country you are coming from and what your role will be in building this "New World". Think about the personal belongings you couldn't do without today. How might these belongings have looked in the past? What tools would you pack? What clothes? What utensils? Would you bring along a musical instrument, a favourite book, a special plant, or other treasured items?*

LA: Identify/use information from an image to select pertinent details.
SS: Understand that communities and environment are interrelated.
SD: Recognize, examine, and appreciate individual/group differences in points of view, values, traditions.

A coat of arms is one of the symbols used to portray the values of a family, a country, or a clan. Examine Canada's coat of arms on **page 24** of *Discovering Culture and Values*. Note that the First Nations peoples living in Canada were not considered when symbols were chosen to represent the "founders" of the nation we know today as Canada. Canada's coat of arms depicts only the governing parties of Great Britain and France who colonized Canada. These are the symbols represented on the coat of arms:

- the English rose, the royal flag, and the lion;

- the Irish clover and the harp;

- the Scottish thistle and the lion;

- the French lily, the royal flag, and the unicorn.

Perhaps the maple leaf shown on our coat of arms should be used to acknowledge the First Nations people. It also represents a plant that was present before European immigration. What other symbol would better represent the presence of First Nations peoples? Use the problem-solving process described in **Tool A1** to help you find an appropriate symbol to add to Canada's coat of arms.

LA: Identify/use information from an image to select pertinent details.
SS: Understand that communities and environment are interrelated. Understand how humans attempt, through symbolism, to make sense of their environment.
FA: Experiment with illustrations using colour, shade, and shape to create symbolism. Identify the elements used to create art: juxtaposition of elements and their location in space.
SD: Recognize, examine, and appreciate individual/group differences in points of view, values, traditions.

If the Canadian government were to redesign its coat of arms to represent the heritage of today's Canadians, how might the coat of arms change in appearance? Imagine that you have been commissioned to redesign Canada's coat of arms to accurately represent our multicultural heritage. Use the problem-solving process described in **Tool A1** and information sources like Statistics Canada to help you with your task of establishing the ethnic origins of the majority of Canadians and then designing an appropriate coat of arms reflecting your findings. Explain your choice of colours and symbols. See **STEPSpage 45** for one artist's version of what different colours signify and **Tool D1** for the criteria by which to evaluate your creation.

**.1** LA: Identify/use information from an image to analyze and describe characteristics.
SS: Understand how humans attempt, through symbolism, to make sense of their environment.
FA: Experiment with illustrations using colour, shade, and shape to create symbolism. Identify the elements used to create art: juxtaposition of elements and their location in space.
SD: Recognize, examine, and appreciate individual/group differences in points of view, values, traditions.

Create a cultural symbol to represent either yourself, your class, or your family. It can be a coat of arms, a totem pole, a crest, or any other symbol. Write an explanation of it. See **STEPSpage 73** and **Tool D1**.

**Or**

**.2** LA: Identify/use information from an image to analyze and describe characteristics.
SS: Understand how humans attempt, through symbolism, to make sense of their environment.
FA: Experiment with illustrations, using colour, shade, and shape to create symbolism. Identify the elements used to create art: juxtaposition of elements and their location in space.
SD: Recognize, examine, and appreciate individual/group differences in points of view, values, traditions.

Find illustrations of the provincial coats of arms. (Consult an illustrated dictionary, a CD-Rom, an encyclopedia, or government brochures.) Using **Tool D1**, examine and analyze the coats of arms for the provinces and territories in Canada. Comment on the significance of the symbols and colours used in each.

**Or**

**.3** Sc: Select and classify data according to criteria.
SS: Understand that communities and environment are interrelated. Interpret, construct, and use maps to represent human characteristics: ethnic or language groupings.

Conduct a survey in your class, or in your school, to find out where students' ancestors came from. Create a map of the world to show the countries of origin of these ancestors. See **Tools D4** and **E10** for mapping techniques and projections.

**Or**

**.4** Sc: Select and classify data according to criteria. Draw conclusions by evaluating, describing, and comparing data collected.
SS: Understand that communities and environment are interrelated. Interpret, construct, and use maps to represent human characteristics: ethnic or language groupings.

Study the emigration/immigration rates for different areas of Canada. These statistics are published by Statistics Canada. Using **Tools D4** and **D5**, prepare a chart, or map, by region to show:

- which areas of Canada have the highest rates of emigration;
- which areas of Canada have the highest rates of immigration;
- from which nations people are immigrating.

One way of presenting Canadian population statistics is shown below.
The populations have been rounded off to the nearest thousand.

| • 1861 | 3 090 000 | • 1881 | 4 325 000 |
|---|---|---|---|
| • 1901 | 5 371 000 | • 1921 | 8 788 000 |
| • 1941 | 11 507 000 | • 1961 | 18 238 000 |
| • 1981 | 25 000 000 | • 2001 | ??? |

Represent these statistics on a graph or on a map. See **Tools D4** (maps) or **D5**
(graphs). Why do you think there were greater increases after 1901? Between
1861 and 1961, over 9 million people immigrated to Canada. How do you
explain the other 6 million people in the statistics?

**Or**

 **.5** Sc: Select and classify data according to criteria. Draw conclusions by evaluating, describing, and
comparing data collected.

SS: Understand that communities and environment are interrelated. Understand how humans
attempt to make sense of their environment through the study of elements of their past
and through interaction with other cultures.

The Canadian government and its designated officials also influenced this country's immigration history. See **STEPSpages 74** to **76** for a list of government acts
and policies which impacted on Canada's cultural diversity. Research one of
these acts or policies to examine its effect on Canada's population at the time it
was instated. Give your opinion on whether the act or law was beneficial or
detrimental to Canada's development as a nation. Support your opinion with
examples. If possible, comment on how this act or policy has affected relations
between Canada's populations today.

 SD: Recognize, examine, and appreciate individual/group differences in points of view, values, traditions.

Using **Tools A1** and **D1**, answer the following questions to reflect on your project:

1. What did you learn by doing this project?

2. How did you select the colours for your coat of arms? Explain.

3. In your opinion, what changes should be made to Canada's coat of arms, if
   any?

4. What do you think is the purpose of having a coat of arms?

5. Do you think that a country should be able to change its coat of arms? Why?

6. Did your friends comment on your work? What did they think?

7. Did you have enough information to do this project? What could have made it
   better?

# E.1 DESIGN YOUR OWN CULTURAL SYMBOL

Create a cultural symbol (coat of arms, mural, crest, etc.) to represent either yourself and your personality, your class, or your family. Not all cultural groups use the coat of arms as a symbol to describe their culture or their family. The Scots also have the tartans, West Coast First Nations peoples used the totem pole, and in East Indian cultures the person's name gives an indication of which clan the person belongs to. Write an explanation for the symbol you have chosen.

## Here's how to get started:

1. Ask yourself these questions about your symbol:

   – Which qualities would you like to present?

   – How would you like people to react when they look at your symbol?

   – What message do you wish to communicate with your symbol?

   – Which colours would you like to use in your symbol? Why?

   – Which characteristics or objects would you like to represent? Why?

   Use **Tool D1** to help you plan the criteria for preparing and evaluating your coat of arms, or other symbol.

2. Draw several sketches. Use your imagination. Experiment to find the lines, the shapes, the colours that best express what you are trying to present.

3. Once you have decided on what you want, draw the coat of arms or the symbol you have chosen.

4. Write a short description explaining why you chose the colours and symbols that you did. Present your symbol to your friends. Add your work of art to your *Thoughtsteps Journal*. Include as well the comments you received from your friends.

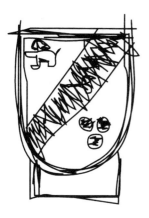

5 CANADIAN IMMIGRATION — NOT WITHOUT ITS SCARS

Government decisions are based on the input received from citizens and other countries. The nature of this input has changed throughout history. Examine some of the government acts, policies, and decisions below. The information for this list was obtained from Victor Malarek's book **Haven's Gate: Canada's Immigration Fiasco**, MacMillan, 1987 (ISBN: 0-7715-9497-6). What do you think this author is trying to tell his readers in this title?

To better understand the policies listed here, it is important to know what was happening in Canada and in the world at the time these decisions were made. Politics, religion, economics, power struggles, and our knowledge about other cultures have had an impact on Canada's immigration history. Research one period of Canada's history to learn why some of these policies were implemented. The following questions may help you form an opinion about the policy selected.

– What historical information can you gather about the period when this policy came into effect?

– Was there a particular group of people pushing, or lobbying, for this act or policy? If so, why? What did they stand to gain?

– Did this policy discriminate against a particular group? Who was affected by the policy and how did it affect them? Were some people opposed to the policy?

– How do you think this act or policy and this period in history have affected the relations between Canada's ethnic populations today?

| | |
|---|---|
| **1867** | At Confederation, Canada's population was approximately 3.5 million: French 1.1 million, Irish .8 million, English .7 million, Scots .5 million, others .4 million. No mention is made of the numbers of First Nations peoples. |
| **1869** | First immigration legislation (under the Department of Agriculture) required that a ship's captain provide a complete passenger list and sufficient funds to cover the costs of temporarily sheltering, feeding, and moving the immigrants to another part of the country. |
| **1872** | The Immigration Act was amended to prohibit the landing of criminal and "other vicious classes". |
| **1879** | An order-in-council was passed excluding paupers and destitute immigrants. |
| **1874** | B.C. legislature passed a law excluding Chinese men from obtaining gold-mining licences. |

| | |
|---|---|
| **1884** | A Royal Commission recommended restricting Chinese immigration. |
| **1885** | Parliament imposed a stiff "head tax" of $50 on every Chinese entering the country. |
| **1896** | Clifford Sifton, minister of the interior, was responsible for lands administration and immigration. His immigration policy, designed to attract peasants from the Ukraine, Poland, and Germany, could be summarized in his own words: "I think that a stalwart peasant in a sheepskin coat, born on the soil, whose forebears have been farmers for ten generations, with a stout wife and a half dozen children, is good quality." |
| **1900** | The B.C. government increased the head tax for Chinese immigrants to $100 and then to $500 three years later. |
| **1907** | A protest riot in Vancouver against Japanese immigration resulted in the loss of several lives. The federal government expressed its regrets to the Japanese government and compensated the families of victims. The Japanese government agreed to limit the number of immigrants to 400 per year. |
| **1908** | Legislation was passed requiring that each immigrant have at least $200 in his own name and that he come to Canada on a ship that had made a non-stop journey from the land of his birth. This legislation was intended to curb the arrivals of East Indian immigrants who were members of the British Empire. |
| **1914** | A shipload of 400 would-be immigrants from India were denied entry into Vancouver and were held aboard their Japanese vessel, the *Komagata Maru,* for nearly three months before one of Canada's two navy ships forced them to return home. |
| **1914-1918** | During the First World War, more than 8000 Ukrainian Canadians were rounded up as enemy aliens and interned in labour camps across Canada. |
| **1918** | At the Imperial War Conference, it was declared that each government within the Commonwealth "should enjoy complete control of the composition of its population". So, until 1930, only 418 East Indians were allowed to enter Canada. |
| **1919** | An order-in-council under the Immigration Act identified a selection process of "preferred" countries (the United Kingdom and the United States) followed by a ranked list of "non-preferred" countries (first northern and western Europe, then central and eastern Europe, and finally southern Europe). Jews, regardless of citizenship, were considered last. |
| **1923** | Japanese immigration was limited to 150 per year. The Chinese Immigration Act was so restrictive that only 7 Chinese immigrants are reported to have entered Canada between 1925 and 1935. However, the government aggressively sought Europeans to settle the land and accepted several thousand Jews from Romania if they had relatives here and were endorsed by the Jewish Immigrant Aid Society. |
| **1926** | The prohibition of Doukhobor immigration was revoked. |
| **1928** | The labour movement finally succeeded in repealing a provision under which strike leaders could be deported. |

B

**Beautiful
Noise**

**B.3**

*A Little Bit
of Everywhere*

| | |
|---|---|
| **1930** | An order-in-council restricted immigrants to wives and children of heads of families already established in Canada. |
| **1932-1952** | The Ku Klux Klan was granted a charter from the government of Alberta. |
| **1939-1944** | Parliament passed a regulation barring enemy aliens. Several hundred German and Italian Canadians and more than 22 000 Japanese Canadians were interned in prison camps. |
| **1942** | The War Measures Act was invoked against residents of Japanese heritage. Their land and belongings were sold and they were required to leave their west-coast homes to work in camps in the interior of B.C. and in Alberta. It was not until 1949 that they were allowed to resettle on the west coast. |
| **1945** | Prime Minister Mackenzie King affirmed Canada's need for a larger population by stating "in a world of shrinking distance and international insecurity, we cannot ignore the danger that lies in a small population holding so great a heritage as ours." |
| **1947** | The ChineseImmigration Act was repealed. |
| **1951** | Special agreements were reached with the Commonwealth countries of India, Pakistan, and Ceylon. |
| **1952** | A new Immigration Act was passed to combine the amendments of the old act. Section 61 gave the government the power to limit or prohibit the entry of immigrants for reasons of nationality, citizenship, ethnic group, class or geographical area of origin, peculiar customs, habits, modes of life or methods of holding property, unsuitability having regard to climatic, economic, social, industrial,educational, labour or health factors or probable inability to become readily assimilated. |
| **1964** | The Department of Citizenship and Immigration prepared a White Paper showing that Canada's existing systems were inadequate and needed to be more closely linked to employment policies. |
| **1966** | Creation of the Department of Manpower and Immigration. |
| **1976** | A new Immigration Act and Regulations was tabled in Parliament and became law in 1978. It states the basic principles underlying immigration policy: non-discrimination, family reunification, humanitarian concern for refugees, and the promotion of national goals. |
| **1984** | The Parliamentary Special Committee on Visible Minorities tabled its unanimous report *Equality Now!* stating "as many as 15 per cent of the Canadian people exhibit blatantly racist attitudes, while another 20 to 25 per cent have some racist tendencies." It highlighted the tensions in Canadian society between cultural groups. |
| **1987** | A bill establishing a new refugee determination process for Canada was tabled. Its purpose was to ensure that "no genuine refugee will be returned to a country where they may face persecution." |

LA: Identify/use information from appropriate sources to select pertinent details and to establish relationships.

SD: Recognize, examine, and appreciate individual/group differences in point of view, opinion, values, and traditions.

We can often learn a great deal about what a culture values by examining the most popular names chosen for the children of that culture. Some names represent elements of the environment; others represent heroes, leaders, or religious figures; others represent desirable characteristics. For example, traditionally both English and French Canadians often named their children after saints or royalty. Traditional First Nations names often included animal or other environmental names. Chinese names for girls were often derived from the names of flowers, while boys' names often represented characteristics like home and security. Sikh, Hindu, and Muslim names often described valued religious symbols or acts. Both boys and girls could bear the same name.

Using **Tool C4**, find out about the origin of your own name.

– From which country does it originate? What does it mean?

– Why were you given this name?

– Do you think that your name describes your personality?

– Does your name exist in other languages? Is it spelled the same way?

– Can your name be used as both a boy's name and a girl's name?

– Is your name a shortened version of another name? If so, which name?

Include the information about your name in your *Thoughtsteps Journal*. Remember to write down your sources of information. With your group, share the information you gathered in your journal.

LA: Identify/use information from appropriate sources to select pertinent details and to establish relationships.

SS: Study a milieu to identify and compare relationships between human traits. Understand how humans attempt to make sense of their environment through the expression of values and interaction with other cultures and ethnic groups.

SD: Recognize, examine, and appreciate individual/group differences in point of view, opinion, values, and traditions.

Names are only one form of cultural expression. People who immigrate to Canada from other countries also bring with them a rich variety of traditions, customs, and celebrations. **STEPSpages 80, 81** provides you with a partial list of celebrations. Research one or more special celebrations. Present your findings to your classmates. Use **Tool C4** to prepare your research. Remember to use at least three different sources of information in your research (see **Tool A5**).

Celebrations are memorable moments that have to be experienced to really be understood. A written report may not be the best presentation format. Instead, talk to someone who has been a part of this cultural celebration. Ask your teacher and the person you are interviewing if it would be possible to have your guest come and speak with the class. Your guest may have objects related to the celebration that he or she could share with your group.

**.1** LA: Identify/use information from appropriate sources to select pertinent details and to establish relationships.

Ma: Use problem-solving strategies to collect, gather, and organize data. Construct and interpret bar graphs to represent data collected.

SD: Recognize, examine, and appreciate individual/group differences in point of view, opinion, values, and traditions.

Extend the preparation activity by conducting a survey of a selected group of students in your school to determine which names are the most common and which names are very original. See **STEPSpage 82** and **Tool D5**.

### Or

**.2** LA: Demonstrate an understanding of adjectives and nouns. Experiment with expressions to express a point of view, an opinion, an emotion, or an analysis.

SS: Understand how humans attempt to make sense of their environment through the expression of values and interaction with other cultures and ethnic groups.

FA: Use colour, shade, and shape in an illustration to represent people and symbolism, focus, or dominating effects.

Prepare a short speech to describe a special tradition, custom, or celebration in your family. See **Tools B2** and **C4**. Use as many adjectives as possible to add detail to your description. See **Tool E2**. Draw a picture of your favourite tradition to show during your speech. As you talk to your small group, refer to your illustration to help your listeners visualize why this tradition, custom, or celebration means so much to you. Use **Tool D1** to analyze your presentation.

### Or

**.3** LA: Demonstrate an understanding of adjectives and nouns.

SS: Understand how humans attempt to make sense of their environment through the expression of values and interaction with other cultures and ethnic groups.

SD: Recognize, examine, and appreciate individual/group differences in point of view, opinion, values, and traditions. Identify, develop, and sustain means of improving esteem, feelings of belonging, and of value.

In your *Thoughtsteps Journal*, record your favourite days of the year. Write a short message beside each entry to explain why these days are special to you. If you wish to extend this activity, research the origin of several of these days. Check your written work to be certain that you have capitalized the first letter of all proper nouns (e.g., names of holidays, days of the week, names of the months). See **Tool E2**. With a small group, share a few of your thoughts on these special dates. See **Tool B2**.

**Or**

**E.4** LA: Identify/use information from appropriate sources to select pertinent details and to establish relationships.

SS: Understand how humans attempt to make sense of their environment through the expression of values and interaction with other cultures and ethnic groups. )

See **A.2, Following the Paths to the Future, Extension E.4**. Prepare a similar study of place names in your area to determine if there was a predominant cultural group that settled in this area and named the towns. If there are one or more predominant cultures, are the customs, traditions, and celebrations of these cultures still practised in your region? See **Tool C4**.

**Or**

**E.5** LA: Identify/use information from appropriate sources to select pertinent details and to establish relationships.

SS: Understand how humans attempt to make sense of their environment through the expression of values and the interaction with other cultures and ethnic groups.)

Using at least three information sources, research the history of the different languages spoken in Canada. Statistics Canada will provide you with data on the languages spoken in Canada. Other reference sources will provide you with historical details about the cultural groups. See **Tools A5** and **C4**.
Were these the results you expected to find? If not, explain. For example, in the 1981 census, 67% of Canadians stated that English was the language spoken, 18% listed French as their mother tongue, and 13% indicated they spoke both English and French. Of the 40 other possible language choices in the census, Italian, German, Ukrainian, Chinese, Portuguese, Dutch, Polish, and Greek were the most frequently chosen.

SS: Understand how humans attempt to make sense of their environment through the expression of values and the interaction with other cultures and ethnic groups.
SD: Recognize, examine, and appreciate individual/group differences in point of view, opinion, values, and traditions. Identify, develop, and sustain means of improving esteem, feelings of belonging, and of value.

Complete the evaluation form for **Tool D1** (and **Tool C4**, if it was used). In your *Thoughtsteps Journal*, include your comments about how names, customs, and celebrations are used to express the values of a society or of a region. In your opinion, is it possible to determine what a cultural group values or honours by examining the names, traditions, customs, celebrations, and languages of its citizens? Explain your answer.

# IT'S TIME TO CELEBRATE!

Research at least one Canadian multicultural celebration. See **Tool C4** and the lists on this page. How many of these celebrations do you celebrate? Not all celebrations are listed here. Are there celebrations you would like to add to the list? Feel free to do so. This list of days was collected from **Let's Celebrate! Canada's Special Days**. (Caroline Parry, Toronto: Kids Can Press, 1987).

---

**Author's Note:** Because the Muslims follow a different calendar, their celebration dates are not included in the lists below. If you would like to research these celebrations, here are a few names to begin your research: Ramadan, Eed-ul-Fitr, Eed-ul-Adha (the Feast of Sacrifice), Meelad-al-Nabi, Ras Al-Sana (New Year's Day), Lailat-al-Isra'-wal-Mi'raj.

---

*January Days*

1, New Year's Day (St. Basil's Day in Greece)

5, Twelfth Night (Christian)

6, Epiphany (Twelfth Day of Christmas)

7, Julian Christmas (Eastern Orthodox)

13 or 14, Pongal (Indian)

19, Epiphany (Ukrainian)

25, Burns Night (Scottish)

30, Greek Day of Education

Other celebration days: Iroquois Midwinter Festival (before Jan. full moon); Solnal, lunar New Year (Korean); Chamishah Asar bi-Shevat (Jewish); Sarasvati Puja (Hindu); Sun Nin (Chinese New Year between January 21 and February 20)

## February Days

2, Groundhog Day (American) or Candlemas (Celt) or Le Chandeleur (Maritimes)

14, Valentine's Day (Christian and Roman)

15, Nirvana Day (Buddhist)

26-March 1, Ayyam-i-ha, Baha'i Intercalary Days

29, Leap Year Day

Other celebration days: Carnaval (Québec); Le Festival du Voyageur (St. Boniface), Yukon Sourdough Rendezvous (Whitehorse); Winterlude (Ottawa); Lent (Christian), 7 weeks before Easter; Carnival, Shrovetide, Mardi Gras, Karneval, Fasching, Zapusty, Farsang, Pancake Day (last celebration before Lent), 7th Tuesday before Easter; Ash Wednesday, 7th Wednesday before Easter; Shiva Ratri (Hindu), mid-February; Purim (Jewish), February or March

## March Days

1, Prvi Mart (Macedonian Bulgarian) or St. David's Day (Welsh)

8, International Women's Day

17, St. Patrick's Day (Irish)

20 or 21, Spring Equinox

22-29, Ohigan (Japanese Buddhists)

20-April 2, Now Ruz (Persian)

25, Greek Independence Day, Evangelismou

Other celebration days: Ram Navami (Hindu); Haru Matsuri (Japanese); Sugaring-off (Ontario, Ojibwa, Iroquois); la cabane à sucre (Quebec); licheries (NB Acadians); Holi (East Indian)

**.1  THE NAMES IN MY COMMUNITY**

(N.B.: This activity can be tailored to include as many names as you feel you are capable of handling or the type of data you will be collecting.) Examine the names of the students in your school by conducting a survey with a selected population of students. Begin by asking your school secretary for a list of the students.

Decide on the type of survey you wish to conduct and the questions to be researched in your survey. Create a survey form to collect your data easily. Here are two possible survey examples:

**A. MOST POPULAR NAMES**

Tally the different names of the students in your school in order to determine which names are the most popular. (A variation of this would be to group names of common origin, like Cathy, Kathy, Catherine, Katrine, in the same category.)

To analyze the data collected, create a bar graph to illustrate the number of times a name is repeated. See **Tool D5**. (This data could then be compared with data from the Department of Vital Statistics on the most common birth names, to see if the choices are similar to those of a broader population sample.)

**B. THE CULTURAL IMPORTANCE PLACED ON NAMES**

The following are samples of questions you could ask:

– What is your family's heritage culture or country of origin?

– What does your name signify or mean?

– Do you know why you were given this name? (Yes/No)

Survey the students on your list by entering their answers to the questions on your survey form. If the student doesn't know the answer, leave this space blank.

To analyze the data collected from your survey, prepare a bar graph to show the number of students from each culture identified. See **Tool D5**. If the student identified more than one culture of origin, include them. The purpose of this activity is to analyze the cultural diversity of your population and the cultural diversity of the names of your students. Complete your graph as follows:

1. Mark a black line in the centre of each culture bar up to the total number of students for that culture.

2. To the left of this line, mark a green line to indicate how many of the students from this cultural background knew the significance of their name.

3. To the right of your black line, mark a red line to indicate how many of the students from this cultural background knew why they had been given their name.

4. From the data you collected, is it possible to determine which cultural groups place an importance on the significance of people's names?

Record the total number of students and the date of the survey beneath your graph.

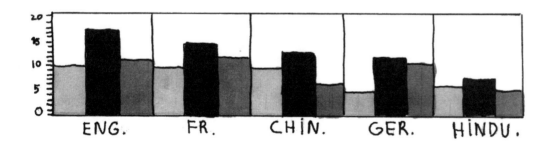

B
Beautiful
Noise

B.4
*My Culture
Is Who I Am*

**B**

Beautiful
Noise

**B.5**

*Where Are
We Headed?*

N.B. The country of study in this activity is Canada. However, it is possible to substitute another country or region without changing the nature of the activity.

LA: Identify/use information from ideas to predict, infer, imagine, and extrapolate.

SS: Study a milieu to explore the relationships between different human traits.

SD: Recognize, examine, and appreciate differences in personality and in means of communicating emotions, interests, and ideas.

Where have you travelled in Canada? What did you learn while travelling? Did you meet some interesting people? Did you have some exciting adventures?

Travelling is a wonderful opportunity to learn more about your country and the people living in it. People who travel with an open mind, whether it be just down the street to the library, across the continent to visit friends or simply to have fun travelling, generally have incredible adventures to tell. Others, who travel with negative attitudes before they set out, will probably have tales to tell about their negative experiences on their journey. The old saying "seek and ye shall find" holds true for all travellers.

**STEPSpages 87, 88** contains a series of perception exercises. Using this page, and **Tool B1**, interview your friends or your family to test the validity of the above statements.

LA: Identify/use information from appropriate sources to establish and evaluate relationships and question the premises for them. Organize selected information logically and creatively. Demonstrate an understanding of language conventions.

Sc: Develop positive attitudes and skills by examining careers in various fields of science.

SS: Understand how humans attempt to make sense of their environment through exploration and inventions.

SD: Recognize, examine, and appreciate individual differences in means of attaining a goal.

Read the story **"Where Are We Off To Now?"** on **pages 25** to **27** of *Discovering Culture and Values*. Imagine that you are either Jesse, Elyssa, or the father in this story. Using **Tool A2**, brainstorm a list of the people or groups you would like to interview if you were to go on this trip. Where would you travel to? What would you want to see?

Using the guidelines from **Tools C1** and **C4** and **STEPSpage 89**, prepare a trip diary in which you describe at least one of your imaginary or real encounters with a person who is contributing in an original way to Canada's present culture. This activity could include an actual interview with someone in your own community. See **Tool B4**. Edit your work with **Tool C8**.

**.1** LA: Identify/use information from appropriate sources to establish and evaluate relationships and question the premises for them.

FA: Experiment with murals to represent people, events, and symbols.

Design a mural of famous Canadians. Include the reasons for their fame. See **Tools C4** and **D3**. In your mural, include an explanation of how Canadians are honoured for their contributions. For your mural, you might choose one or several areas of recognition and explain why the individuals you have included were given this award (e.g., Canadian Hall of Fame, Governor General's Award, Citizen of the Year Award, Nobel Prize, Juno Award, Victoria Cross).

**Or**

**.2** LA: Identify/use information from appropriate sources to establish and evaluate relationships and question the premises for them. Organize selected information logically and creatively. Demonstrate an understanding of language conventions.

Sc: Develop positive attitudes and skills by examining careers in various fields of science.

SS: Understand how humans attempt to make sense of their environment through exploration and invention.

SD: Recognize, examine, and appreciate individual differences in means of attaining a goal.

Using **Tools C4** and **C8**, research and write a collection of stories about people who make, or who have made, contributions to your community. Publish these stories in the form of a book or as articles.

**Or**

**.3** LA: Identify/use information from appropriate sources to establish and evaluate relationships and question the premises for them. Organize selected information logically and creatively.

Sc: Develop positive attitudes and skills by examining careers in various fields of science.

SS: Understand how humans attempt to make sense of their environment through exploration and inventions.

SD: Recognize, examine, and appreciate individual differences in means of attaining a goal.

Research a Canadian invention and its inventor. See **Tool C4**. Make an oral presentation to your class on your topic using **Tools B2** and **B4**.

**Or**

**.4** FA: Evaluate an original or professional composition for cognitive or affective value. Create an original selection of music. Examine the evolution of music through time.

Explore traditional and contemporary Canadian music. See **Tool C4**. Then, using **Tool B3**, create your own musical composition to highlight one or several aspects of Canada's culture. See **STEPSpage 90**.

**Or**

## B
Beautiful
Noise

**B.5**

*Where Are
We Headed?*

 **.5** LA: Identify/use information from appropriate sources to establish and evaluate relationships and question the premises for them. Organize selected information logically and creatively.

SS: Understand how humans attempt to make sense of their environment through exploration and invention.

SD: Recognize, examine, and appreciate individual differences in means of attaining a goal.

Plan a summer vacation in the form of a cross-Canada trip. Brainstorm a list of the sites, museums, art galleries, and so on you would visit. See **Tool A2**. Then, using **Tool A3**, rank your top five choices and create a sequence chart or travel itinerary to illustrate where you would go and why. For ideas, ask your local tourism office or look on the Internet.

**Or**

 **.6** SD: Recognize, examine, and appreciate individual/group differences in means of attaining a goal.

Consult the diaries written by members in the class, as well as the list on **STEPSpage 89**. In your *Thoughtsteps Journal*, create a chart of Canadians who are contributing in an original way to Canada's present culture. List these individuals according to their category of fame. As you hear about other individuals, add them to your chart. For each entry, comment on the individuals' contributions and how they attained their goals. See **Tools A3** and **C4**.

LA: Identify/use information from appropriate sources to establish and evaluate relationships and question the premises for them.

SS: Understand how humans attempt to make sense of their environment through exploration and invention.

SD: Recognize, examine, and appreciate individual differences in means of attaining a goal.

Throughout this section you have been examining the cultural makeup of Canada. In your own words, summarize what aspects of Canadian society enable you to define what Canadian culture means to you. Write your ideas in your *Thoughtsteps Journal*.

Review the preparation section on **STEPSpage 84**. To test the validity of the statements on **STEPSpage 84**, interview your friends and family about their most recent trip. From what they have told you, is it possible to know whether they felt positively or negatively about their experience? What evidence do you have to support your assumption? The following questions may be helpful in gathering your evidence. See also **Tool B1**.

1. Where did you go on your trip?

   (Observe the facial expressions of the people you interview. Do they look happy as they mention their travel destination?)

2. Could you describe one or more details of your trip to your destination? What adventures or encounters did you have along the way?

   (Listen carefully to the kinds of experiences they talk about. Are these experiences generally positive or negative? When something went wrong, how did they react? What do their reactions tell you? Was the journey important, or irrelevant, in relationship to the destination?)

3. While you were on your trip, did you meet people? Did you make any new friends?

   (As a tourist, travellers may meet other travellers, but may not establish friendships with the people who actually live in their travel destination. As you listen to the answer to this question, consider whether the people you are interviewing gained or learned anything from their conversations, shared experiences, and friendships with the people they met.)

4. Did your trip change your way of thinking about others and yourself in any way? Explain.

   (This question is an important one and you may wish to ask other questions to get a clearer answer. The answers you are listening for should help you gather information about these peoples' views about others. Do your interviewees talk about individuals or general groups? Do they use general statements to describe the entire community or do they use specific statements about individuals?)

*When individuals from different cultures become friends, generalized statements about a cultural group rarely fit into the friendship. Comments like, "The people from _____ never smile, they work all the time, they only talk about how much money they make, and they never do anything for fun…" are generalizations. When we believe that everyone from a specific culture acts a certain way or eats a certain food or wears a certain type of clothing, we close our eyes to the diversity that really makes up the culture. These generalizations are known as stereotypes, or clichés. How can you tell if a comment is stereotypical or cliché? Ask yourself this question: If I were to say this comment to a friend, would my friend be offended? If the answer is yes, then you are probably dealing with a stereotype or a cliché, or even an insult.)*

As you go on to the activity phase of this learning path, think about this question: Would the contributors from the many ethnic origins of Canada's culture have been able to contribute so much had they listened to everything that strangers said about them?

# ENCOUNTERS WITH CANADIANS WHO ARE DEFINING CANADIAN CULTURE

Here is a list of possible areas for you to explore how individuals are contributing, or have contributed, in a significant way to Canada's present culture. One or two individuals have been listed in each category. Try to come up with other names. Each section could be expanded to form a data bank on the individuals with their name, date of birth, area of accomplishments, recognition, and personal information about how they achieved their goals. See **Tools C1** and **C4**.

Music
Dal Vog
Susan Aglukark
Céline Dion
Gordon Lightfoot
Gilles Vigneault

Space Exploration
Marc Garneau
Roberta Bondar
Julie Payette

Sports
Wayne Gretzky
Donovan Bailey
Nancy Greene
Normie Kwong

Politics
Sir John A. Macdonald
Louis Riel
Ovide Mercredi
Nellie McClung

Science
David Suzuki
Ursula Martius Franklin
Ernest Rutherford
Gerhard Herzberg

Sculpture
Elizabeth Wyn Wood
Kosso Eloul
Bill Reid
Florence Wyle

Historical Documentation
Marius Barbeau
Henrietta Louise Edwards
Reverend John Snow

Dance
Evelyn Hart
Arnold Spohr
David Earle
Karen Kain

Inventions
J. Armand Bombardier
Alexander Graham Bell
Uno Vilho Helava

Medicine
Charles H. Best
F.J. Banting
Wilder Penfield
Har Gobind Khorana
Octavia Grace Ritchie
Jennie Trout

Literature
Margaret Laurence
Farley Mowat
C.J. Taylor
William Kurelek
Gabrielle Roy
Josef Skvorecky
Bharati Mukherjee
Peter Pitseolak
George Clutesi
Antonine Maillet
W.O. Mitchell
Alice Munro
Mordecai Richler
Joy Kogawa

Poetry
Émile Nelligan
Earle Birney
Michael Ondaatje
Calixa Lavallée

Painting
Emily Carr
A.Y Jackson
Kenojuak Ashevak
Daphne Odjig
Alfred Pellan
Jessie Oonark

Architecture
Arthur Charles Erickson

Charitable Causes
Terry Fox
Assasingh Johal
Rick Hanson

Film-making
Claude Jutras
Norman Jewison
Mireille Dansereau
William "Ted" Kotcheff

Composers
James Kim Bell
Glenn Gould
Anton Kuerti

Journalism
René Lévesque
Barbara Frum
Allan Fotheringham
Margaret "Ma" Murray
Pierre Berton

Theatre
Michel Tremblay
Dora Mavor Moore
George Ryga
Tom Jackson

# E.4 A STUDY OF TRADITIONAL AND CONTEMPORARY CANADIAN MUSIC

Using a variety of different sources (music stores, libraries, your music teacher), listen to several selections of Canadian music. See the bibliography on **STEPSpage 136**. Then create your own musical composition to highlight one or several aspects of Canada's culture.

– What is "real" Canadian music?

– Is there such a thing as traditional Canadian music?

– What do the following terms mean to you: reel, jig, quadrille, hornpipe, strathspey?

– Are you familiar with the traditional music or instruments from Canada's First Nations?

The music that is often considered to be traditional in Canada is the music that the first immigrants brought with them from their countries of origin.

Examine the origins of our traditional music by listening to a selection of jigs (originating from Ireland), reels (from Scotland), and quadrilles (from France). Ask your school's music teacher to help you with this. If possible, consult the elders from your area to learn what traditional music was passed down through the native cultural traditions in your region.

– What instruments are most often used in this type of music?

– Can you identify the instruments used in the selections you were able to listen to?

Because instruments were not always available, the early settlers were accustomed to adding in foot tapping, hand clapping, and even playing on a washboard or with spoons. This background noise resembles the sound of horses' hooves. Because the horse was the principal means of transportation, it was usually not forgotten when it came to making music!

In many First Nations cultures, the drum was, and still is, an important instrument. An excellent drummer was one who could beat his drum to the changing rhythms of his heartbeat.

Using an instrument of your choice, improvise a short musical composition to link traditional music with contemporary music. To do this activity, you will need to listen to several selections of Canadian music, both from the past (traditional) and from the present (contemporary). See **Tool C4**. Ask your friends to bring tapes or compact discs from home to give you a broader sampling of the music available in Canada today.

Study a Canadian musician or group and the messages that they sing about. See **Tool C4**. This study might involve a contemporary or a traditional artist. Write a short article about this person or group in the form of a newspaper or magazine music review. Create a **Canadian Music Magazine** with the articles of all the students in your group.

**B**
**Beautiful Noise**

**B.5**
***Where Are We Headed?***

# STEPS TO DISCOVERING... ACTIVITIES

**Preparing your *Thoughtsteps Journal***

# A World of Legends

 Open your *Thoughtsteps Journal*. Add to it a blank page, a lined page, and two more blank pages.
 – On the first page, write the title of your theme.
 – On the lined page, write the words "Table of Contents". As you work through the theme, list your activities here.
 – On the next blank page, list your ideas, words, knowledge relating to legends from around the world and the beliefs of those who tell them. See **Tool A2**.

 Using your list of ideas from the brainstorming activity, make a poster on the next page of your *Thoughtsteps Journal*. Show words and images about the theme *Discovering Culture and Values:* **A World of Legends**.

On the back of this page, write the title "Discovering New Words". As you work through the activities in this theme, list on this page any new words you encounter.

**E.1** Use a dictionary to review spelling.

**Or**

**E.2** Create a class poster combining everyone's ideas.

**Or**

**E.3** Look through other resource books for ideas for illustrations or words. Add them to your poster.

**Or**

**E.4** Add illustrations to your title page.

**Or**

**E.5** Add a **Bibliography** page. See **Tool A5** to learn how to list your sources.

**R** Check your poster for spelling: remember it's a tool you will use during the entire theme! Does it represent the theme? At the bottom of the poster, write down three ideas you would like to explore in this theme.

LA: Identify/use information from a text to predict, infer, anticipate, and extrapolate outcomes. Identify/use information selected from appropriate sources to classify and analyze characteristics, and to summarize ideas.

SS: Understand how humans attempt to make sense of their environment through the expression of values, the study of elements of the past, and interaction with other cultures.

SD: Recognize, examine, and appreciate individual/group differences in means of expressing and communicating ideas.

The purpose of this stage of the activity is to explore how quickly stories change and to learn about folktales, myths, legends, and fables.

Begin by selecting a well-known fairytale that you can relate from memory. Record your version of this fairytale on tape. Then ask two friends to record their versions of this fairytale on separate cassettes so that you will have three tapes of the same fairytale. See **Tool C2**.

Prepare a chart like the one shown on **STEPSpage 96**. As you play back the tapes to those who participated, use your chart to record the similarities and differences between the stories.

How might today's tales have been different had we been able to record the original stories told hundreds of years ago?

Read **STEPSpage 97** to prepare a classification chart for comparing folktales, myths, legends, and fables.

LA: Identify/use information from a text to predict, infer, anticipate, and extrapolate outcomes. Identify/use information selected from appropriate sources to classify and analyze characteristics, and to summarize ideas. Organize information logically, chronologically, and creatively.

SD: Recognize, examine, and appreciate individual/group differences in means of expressing and communicating ideas.

Imagine that you belong to an ancient civilization 2000 years ago and that your region has not received rain for many months. You don't have the scientific knowledge or the technology that we have today. Therefore, you turn to nature to ask for help. Using **Tools A1** and **C2** and the chart from **STEPSpage 96**, write down each of the steps you might take to resolve your drought problem.

Then read **"Tell Me a Tale!"** on **pages 29** to **33** of *Discovering Culture and Values*. As you read, compare your solution for drought to the solution in this legend. Complete your chart to analyze the two solutions.

# C

## A World of Legends

## C.1
### Story-telling

**.1** LA: Organize information logically, chronologically, and creatively.

FA: Formulate a monologue from a given theme. Use appropriate gestures, voice, and special effects.

Use your imagination to elaborate on your version of the return of the rain legend. Practise reciting your legend in front of a mirror and add appropriate gestures and facial expressions. Ask a friend to listen to your legend and to offer suggestions for changes you could make. See **Tools B2** and **B3**. Then present your legend to a small audience.

**Or**

**.2** LA: Identify/use information selected from appropriate sources to classify and analyze characteristics, and to summarize ideas.

SS: Understand how humans attempt to make sense of their environment through the expression of values, the study of elements of the past, and interaction with other cultures.

Explore different cultures through the symbols contained in their folktales, myths, legends, and fables. See **STEPSpage 98** and **Tools C2** and **C4**.

**Or**

**.3** LA: Identify/use information selected from appropriate sources to classify and analyze characteristics, and to summarize ideas.

Create a character cube for a legendary hero. See **STEPSpage 100** and **Tools C2** and **C4**.

**Or**

**.4** LA: Identify/use information selected from appropriate sources to classify and analyze characteristics, and to summarize ideas. Organize information logically, chronologically, and creatively.

Create a maze of different legends. See **STEPSpage 102** and **Tools C2** and **C4**.

**Or**

**E.5** LA: Identify/use information selected from appropriate sources to classify and analyze characteristics, and to summarize ideas. Organize information logically, chronologically, and creatively.

Tell a modern version of an ancient tale by changing the characters and the setting. Would the problem have been resolved differently if this tale had taken place in your community? For example, could the story of Little Red Riding Hood be told the same way in your community? Do you have wolves, forests, and grandmothers living within walking distance? See **Tools C2** and **C4**.

**R** SD: Recognize, examine, and appreciate individual/group differences in means of expressing and communicating ideas.

In your *Thoughtsteps Journal*, record the answers to the questions shown on **STEPSpage 104** and then discuss your answers as a group. Include your evaluations from the **Toolbox** cards used in this activity, especially **Tool C2**.

## COMPARING THE STORIES

**A World of Legends**

**C.1**

*Story-telling*

Copy this chart into your *Thoughtsteps Journal* and complete the comparisons:

| | 1ST TALE | 2ND TALE | 3RD TALE |
|---|---|---|---|
| **What is the problem?** **Why is this a problem?** | | | |
| **Who are the characters?** Describe: <br>— their personality; <br>— their qualities; <br>— their weaknesses; <br>— their strengths; <br>— their physical appearance; <br>— their emotions. | | | |
| **When and where does the story take place?** **(time period/setting)** | | | |
| **How is the problem resolved?** | | | |
| **What other details seem important?** Consider: <br>— the illustrations; <br>— the symbols (numbers); <br>— the actions; <br>— the language used. | | | |
| **Summarize the similarities and differences you observed in your comparison of these tales.** | | | |

# FOLKTALES, MYTHS, LEGENDS, AND FABLES

Long before televisions, radios, computers, and stereos, people had to create their own forms of entertainment. Music, games, stories, songs, and dances were popular with all age groups. In the case of story-telling, if the story was told well, the listeners would ask to hear it again and again until they knew it so well that they, too, could tell it. As these tales were not usually written down, the story would change from teller to teller. When the name of the author had long been forgotten, the story then belonged to the cultural group and was known as a **folktale**.

Sometimes these folktales involved gods or superhumans who were responsible for creating the elements of nature. This type of tale is usually called a **myth**. Examples would be stories about the creation of the world, of humans, or the origin of certain rituals or ceremonies.

Other stories explained how or why some wonderful event occurred. These **legends** were popular because they usually began with a true dilemma or event. Perhaps the series of events was pure coincidence; nonetheless, those who observed the event believed what they saw and told their story over and over.

Another popular form of folktale is the **fable**. Fables were used to teach a social lesson through animals or objects. These animals (or objects), who acted and thought like humans, were used to teach listeners about desirable social qualities (patience, wisdom, sharing) or about undesirable traits (greed, anger, carelessness).

As folktales, myths, legends, and fables were passed down from generation to generation, they, too, were embellished and altered until sometimes it was difficult to tell if the tale was a myth, a legend, a fable, or a folktale.

In your *Thoughtsteps Journal*, prepare a two-page chart similar to the one on **STEPSpage 96**. Use these titles as your headings: **Folktale, Myth, Legend, Fable**. In your chart, record the information shown below. Leave enough space on your chart to add more details as you work through this unit.

1. Using a dictionary and the explanations above, describe the characteristics that define each heading.

2. What folktales, myths, legends, or fables do you know? Write one or more examples under each heading.

3. As you work through this unit, you will discover or remember other examples of folktales, myths, legends, and fables. When you do, add these titles to your chart.

C

A World of Legends

C.1

*Story-telling*

# E.2 EXPLORING CULTURES THROUGH THEIR TALES

Folktales, myths, legends, and fables are often based on a small seed of truth that has been greatly exaggerated in order to intrigue the storyteller's audience. However, by reading or listening to tales from different cultures, we can learn a great deal about the values and social interactions of these cultures. As you explore different tales, take the time to complete the chart below. See **Tools C2** and **C4**.To discover some of the common elements that repeat themselves in the folktales, myths, legends, and fables, you will need to read at least four different tales from the same country or cultural group. See the bibliography on **STEPSpages 136** for some books to look for in your school or community library.

N.B.: The chart below is like the one shown on **STEPSpage 96**, only the headings are arranged vertically. Choose either format to present your observations.

| Title of the tale | Problem | Characters | Time period/Setting | How the problem is resolved | Other Details |
|---|---|---|---|---|---|
| | | | | | |

AFTER COMPLETING THIS CHART, ARE YOU ABLE TO TELL YOUR CLASS-
MATES SOMETHING ABOUT THE CULTURE THAT THESE LEGENDS COME
FROM? SUMMARIZE YOUR ANALYSIS OF THESE TALES BY COMPLETING
THE TWO STATEMENTS BELOW.

1. In _____ (name of country or social group), I have noticed
   that their legends are often about...

2. This gives me a clue that this culture may value, or think it important to
   value...

**C**

A World
of Legends

**C.1**

*Story-telling*

# E.3 CUBIC HEROES

Create a character cube for a legendary hero. See **Tool C2** for an evaluation format for this activity. You need use only the criteria that apply.

Can you name some of the legendary heroes that we admire today? OA legendary hero could be either a real or an imaginary person who possesses, or seems to possess, superhuman talents. What makes these people heroes? What are they able to do that is so exceptional?

Often we describe a person first by his or her appearance. Then we might add a simple comment about personality, like "She's a very nice person." Physical appearances can change a great deal over time, but personality tends to be more constant. So is it really a good idea to describe people according to how they look?

The purpose of this activity is to create a mystery cube displaying the many sides of a legendary person, without naming the individual. Or you might prefer to become a legendary hero or heroine yourself by creating your own character cube. Begin by drawing the pattern for a cube. On each face of the cube describe one aspect of this person's character:

- qualities;
- weaknesses or faults;
- superhuman powers or talents;
- emotions;
- physical appearance;
- time period and place of residence.

With each description, include an example to illustrate your statement.

# E.3 CUBIC HEROES, continued...

**Example: Do you know this person?**

**Qualities:** He is a happy, gentle person who is always ready to help when his help is needed, especially when his girlfriend is in trouble.

**Faults/Weaknesses:** Without his can of spinach he is powerless.

**Superhuman powers:** His arms are incredibly strong. With one punch, he is able to send a bully to the top of a mast or high into the sky.

**Emotions:** He is in love with Olive Oyl.

**Physical appearance:** This sailor is quite short. His girlfriend is taller than he is. He usually wears a cap cocked over one eye and smokes a pipe.

**Place of residence:** He lives near the sea. He is often seen in cartoons on television.

**Time period:** 20th century.

## E.4 CREATE A MAZE OF LEGENDS

> ### The legend of Ariadne, Theseus, and the Minotaur
>
> *In ancient Greece, for many years, the people of the kingdom of Crete had feared the Minotaur living in the labyrinths of their island. Once a year, to appease the rage of the Minotaur, the people sacrificed seven young men and seven young women for this beast. The king had declared that the man who could kill the Minotaur would be allowed to marry his daughter, Ariadne. Many had tried, but they became lost in the labyrinth and either died of thirst and hunger or were found by the Minotaur. A young man named Theseus fell in love with the beautiful princess. Ariadne also loved Theseus, but knew it would be impossible to marry him without her father's consent. So, together the two lovers devised a plan. Ariadne gave Theseus a ball of golden twine so that he would be able to find his way out of the maze once he had killed the Minotaur. Theseus succeeded and Ariadne was able to marry him.*

Your first challenge is to create a maze of folktales, myths, legends, and/or fables connected by wool like Ariadne's golden twine. The second challenge is to see who will be able to untangle the legend first and tell it to the others.

1. Begin by writing out a legend so that each paragraph or segment appears on a separate file card or sheet of paper. Repeat this step for at least three other legends. (This is more fun to do if you're not alone!) See **Tool C2** if you need help in summarizing your legends.

2. Cut a length of wool and tie each segment of your legend, in the order that you would tell it, onto the string. Do the same for the other legends. This works best if you use different coloured wool for each legend.

3. Tie the end of your legend to a stationary object. Twist your string over, under, around, between, the strings of your friends' legends. When all of the legends are entwined, exchange strings with someone else.

4. Give the signal to start untangling the legends. (Hint: If your legends are hopelessly tangled, break the wool and tie the strands back together before going on.)

5. Each time a player untangles a legend, the "hunt" stops. Everyone freezes while the player reads the legend. When this tale is finished, the hunt resumes. Players who have finished may offer to help those who are still untangling their tales.

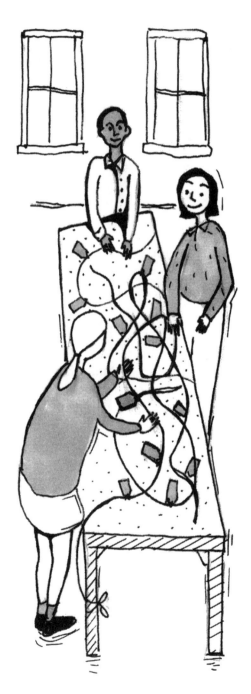

**C**

A World
of Legends

**C.1**

*Story-telling*

**THOUGHTS ON FOLKTALES, MYTHS, LEGENDS, AND FABLES**

In your *Thoughtsteps Journal*, record the answers to the questions shown below.

1. What role do folktales, myths, legends, and fables play in the culture or the values of a society?

2. Give at least two examples of phenomena that cultures have tried to explain through their legends or myths.

3. Give at least two examples of lessons cultures have taught through fables or folktales.

4. Why do tales change over time?

5. How did you share your legend or tale with others? If you could share it again, how would you present it this time? Why?

6. Why do people still love to tell and listen to legends? Explain your answer.

7. Do you know of folktales, myths, legends, or fables that tell a similar story but originate in different cultures? If so, describe how they differ and how they are similar.

8. In your *Thoughtsteps Journal*, include the comments from the **Toolbox** cards you used for this activity.

LA: Identify/use information from a text/idea to predict, infer, imagine, anticipate, or extrapolate.

FA: Formulate a dialogue from a given theme. In a positive manner, support the roles played by others. Use appropriate gestures, voice, and special effects.

SD: Recognize, examine, and appreciate individual/group differences in means of expressing ideas.

With a group of friends, improvise a short skit on what you think the legends or myths on **STEPSpage 108** might be about. To add an element of surprise to your improvisations, write the questions from **STEPSpage 108** on strips of paper and draw them from a hat or a box. Remember that an improvisation is done quickly, without a lot of time to prepare. This activity should take only 10 to 15 minutes. See **Tools B2** and **B3**.

Present your improvisation to the class. You might present this on videotape so that you can compare your version with the legends you will read about, and present, in the activity section.

LA: Identify/use information from a text/idea to predict, infer, imagine, anticipate, or extrapolate.

SS: Understand how humans attempt to make sense of their environment through the expression of values, the study of elements of the past, and interaction with other cultures.

FA: Formulate a dialogue from a given theme. In a positive manner, support the roles played by others. Use appropriate gestures, voice, and special effects.

SD: Recognize, examine, and appreciate individual/group differences in means of expressing ideas.

Consult the table of contents for *Discovering Culture and Values*. Select one of the titles from the section **"A World of Legends"**. Read the story you selected. With a group of students, present this myth, legend, or folktale in the form of a play. As a team, you will need to decide what props, lighting, costumes, and music you would like to use. See **Tools A6, B2, B3,** and **D8** for production ideas and suggestions.

– What format will you use for your presentation (shadow play, puppet play, readers' theatre, stage production)?

– How will you invite people to come to your production?

– Will you have a program announcing the play (or plays)?

**Tool A6** contains ideas on how to divide the tasks. **Tools B2** and **B3** provide ideas for evaluating your "stage presence". **Tool D8** contains suggestions for prop design.

**E.1**    LA: Identify/use information from a text/idea to predict, infer, imagine, anticipate, or extrapolate.

       FA: Formulate a dialogue from a given theme. In a positive manner, support the roles played by others. Use appropriate gestures, voice, and special effects.

       SD: Identify, develop, and sustain means of improving group process skills: goal setting, planning, achieving, and evaluating.

If you prefer to present another legend as a play, review the topics on **STEPSpage 108**. Choose a topic that appeals to you and write a legend that will answer that particular question. If none appeals to you, write a legend on the topic of your choice.

To help you with your writing, consult **Tools A3**, **C2**, and **C8**. Remember that legends are written in the past tense.

When you are ready to complete your final copy, present your legend as a skit. See **Tool B3** for ideas. The extension activities below might also be useful in planning your presentation. See **Tool D10** if you wish to videotape your skit.

**Or**

**E.2**    LA: Identify/use information from an idea/image to describe characteristics.

       FA: Experiment with sculpting and modelling to represent imaginary characters, people or animals.

Create masks for the characters in your play using the process described in **STEPSpages 53** to **55** and **Tool D8**. You will need to think about the characters' physical appearance, as well as their personality, and how you can represent these characteristics on your mask. See **E.3**, **Cubic Heroes**, on **STEPSpage 100** for ideas on different characteristics to represent.

**Or**

**E.3**    LA: Identify/use information from a text/song to summarize ideas. Explore and analyze the ways in which media contain attitudes, messages, or biases in their products.

       FA: Evaluate an original or professional composition for the significance or intent of the musical language used. With a group, create an original selection of music.

In the past, legends were often told in song. This form of song is called a "ballad". If possible, listen to a legend or folktale that is told as a song. Many popular folk artists have recorded history in the form of a ballad. Some examples to listen to might be: The Chieftains, The Rankin Family, The Irish Rovers, Gordon Lightfoot, Gilles Vigneault, Leonard Cohen, Joni Mitchell. Retell the message of this song in your own words.

Today, books, television, and multimedia programs carry on story-telling traditions. Yet, a good story-teller is always welcome in any social gathering. To challenge your story-telling abilities, choose a simple legend from a book, or one that you have made up. Then create your own song for, or about, your legend and add in the accompaniment. See **Tools B3** and **E1**.

SD: Identify, develop, and sustain means of improving group process skills: goal setting, planning, achieving, and evaluating.

Complete the evaluation forms for **Tools A6** and **B3** and include them in your *Thoughtsteps Journal*.

Answer the questions below as you reflect on the impact visual support materials add to your message.

1. What presentation format did you use for your skit? What format did you use for the play in the activity stage?

2. How effective were your presentations? Give one example where your audience responded in the way you had intended.

3. What special effects (props, lighting, sound, music, costumes) did you use to enhance your presentation? Give one example where you could have improved the response from your audience by adding special effects.

4. Using a scale from 1 to 5 (1 = most important, 5 = least important) rate the importance of each of the following elements in your presentation:

   - props;
   - sound effects;
   - music;
   - costumes;
   - lighting changes;
   - actions of the actors;
   - audibility of the actors' voices;
   - changes in the actors' tone of voice.

If you completed any of the extension activities, describe how these activities used media effects to enhance their messages. Add any other completed **Toolbox** evaluation forms to your *Thoughtsteps Journal*.

# IMPROVISE A LEGEND

The questions below could be written on strips of paper and drawn from a hat or a box to add an element of surprise to your legend improvisations. See **Tool B3** to prepare and evaluate your improvisations of why these physical phenomena exist.

Imagine that you belong to a culture which doesn't believe modern-day scientists have all the "right" answers. Improvise a legend or myth to describe an alternative explanation for these questions:

Why is the sky blue?

Where did water come from?

How did the sun come to be?

Why did clouds appear in the sky?

Where does thunder come from?

What sends lightning to the earth?

Why are there earthquakes?

What makes volcanoes erupt?

Where did fire come from?

Where do daylight and darkness come from?

Why do we have tides?

Where did the stars come from?

How did so many creatures come to inhabit the earth?

LA: Identify/use information from a text to establish relationships of cause and effect or consequences and to question the premises for them.

SS: Understand how humans attempt to make sense of their environment through the study of elements of the past and through interaction with other cultures.

Read the myths **"The Beginning of the World"** and **"And So the Night Was Born"** on pages **34** to **40** of *Discovering Culture and Values*. For each myth, prepare a matrix chart using **Tool E9**. Complete as much of each chart as possible with the information found in these two myths. Don't be concerned about not having all the information. Remember it's not possible to learn everything there is to know about a cultural group from one story.

 LA: Identify/use information from a text to establish relationships of cause and effect or consequences and to question the premises for them.

Sc: Understand the relationships between living organisms and their environment.

SS: Understand how humans attempt to make sense of their environment through the study of elements of the past and through interaction with other cultures. Represent a series of events on a timeline. Compare different events in time.

Ma: Classify information chronologically.

Science has its own creation myth. Even those who are experts in their field admit that many theories, though commonly accepted, are difficult or impossible to prove. The story of the earth's beginnings is one example of a theory that may never be completely proven. Using the information on **STEPSpage 112**, complete a third chart to add to the two from the preparation stage. See **Tool E9**. How are these myths and theories similar or different? Create a visual timeline of science's version of the creation of Earth by following the directions on **STEPSpage 113** and using **Tool D7**.

**.1** LA: Identify/use information from a text to establish relationships of cause and effect or consequences and to question the premises for them.

SS: Understand how humans attempt to make sense of their environment through the study of elements of the past and through interaction with other cultures.

Compare the Norse myth about the beginning of the world with creation myths from other ancient cultures. To do this, you will need to read myths from several different cultural groups or civilizations (ancient Greek, Roman, Egyptian, Chinese, Mayan, Muslim, Hindu, Buddhist, or Christian tales). With each creation myth, complete a matrix chart to add to those from the preparation and activity stages. See **Tool E9**. Use these completed charts to compare the similarities and differences of the different myths.

**Or**

**.2** LA: Identify/use information from a text to establish relationships of cause and effect or consequences and to question the premises for them. Demonstrate an understanding of language conventions and mechanics.

SS: Understand how humans attempt to make sense of their environment through the study of elements of the past and through interaction with other cultures.

# C
## A World of Legends

## C.3
### Myths from the Beginning

Choose your favourite myth and write it in your own words for a younger audience. See **Tools C2** and **C8**. Present the final version of your myth in an accordion-type booklet. See **STEPSpage 114** or **Tool C7**.

**Or**

**.3** LA: Identify/use information from a text to establish relationships of cause and effect or consequences and to question the premises for them.

SS: Understand how humans attempt to make sense of their environment through the study of elements of the past and through interaction with other cultures.

FA: Formulate a dialogue from a given theme. Use appropriate gestures, voice, and special effects.

Tell the life story of Earth using puppets. Describe highlights of the geological history, the evolution of life forms, etc. See **STEPSpage 115** and **Tools B2** and **B3**.

**Or**

**.4** LA: Identify/use information from a text to establish relationships of cause and effect or consequences and to question the premises for them.

Sc: Understand the relationships between living organisms and their environment.

SS: Understand how humans attempt to make sense of their environment through the study of elements of the past and through interaction with other cultures.

To explore other relationships between different elements of life on Earth, play the game shown on **STEPSpages 116** to **118**. Use the ideas from this game to describe how everything on Earth is interrelated.

SD: Recognize, examine, and appreciate individual/group differences in means of expressing ideas.

Use **Tool E9** and the charts you completed to summarize your ideas about this activity. Did you agree with the ideas presented? Are there changes you would make? Record your comments in your *Thoughtsteps Journal*.

# A VISUAL TIMELINE OF THE EARTH'S LIFE STORY

To visualize the age of planet Earth, mark out a timeline. Here are the figures for your timeline. See **Tool D7**.

**The Past** (First stake to second stake)

1. 4.6 billion years ago, the solar system and the planet Earth were formed. — 1. —460 metres

2. 3.5 billion years ago, the first aquatic forms of life appeared on this planet. — 2. —350 metres

3. 405 million years ago, the first life appeared on land. — 3. —40.5 metres

4. 360 million years ago, the first insects appeared. — 4. —36 metres

5. 200 million years ago, the dinosaur age began. — 5. —20 metres

6. 136 million years ago, flowering plants appeared. — 6. —13.6 metres

7. 65 million years ago, the dinosaurs disappeared. — 7. —6.5 metres

8. 300 000 years ago, humans appeared. — 8. —30 centimetres

9. 10 000 years ago, the ice age ended and humans began growing their food. — 9. —1 centimetre

10. 2 000 years ago, Jesus Christ was born. This is considered the starting point for our present age. — 10. —2 millimetres

11. 100 years ago, the industrial revolution began. Prior to this, agriculture was the most common kind of work. — 11. —0.1 millimetre

**The Present** — 12. 0 metre (2nd stake)
**The Future** — 13. 0 to +1 metre (3rd stake)

# A VISUAL TIMELINE OF THE EARTH'S LIFE STORY, continued...

Using **Tools A1** and **D7**, observe what impact people have had on the environment during our brief existence on Earth. See **STEPSpage 112** for the statistics you will need to create a visual timeline, representing both the age of the earth and major events occurring in its life story.

### MATERIALS REQUIRED

- 461 metres of wool or string
- a hammer
- three stakes (about 1 m high)
- 11 strips of cloth
- a measuring tape or a measuring wheel

### DIRECTIONS

1. Plant the stake for your starting point and attach the end of your string or wool to this stake. You may need more than one ball of wool for this activity!

2. Using the measuring tape or wheel, measure a distance of 460 metres. Plant your second stake here and wrap the string or wool around it. Plant your third stake one metre beyond the 460 metre mark and tie the last metre of string to it. This third stake represents the future, the second stake the present, and the distance up to the second stake represents the past.

3. Once your marker stakes are in place, mark each of the additional stages of the timeline shown on **STEPSpage 112** by attaching pieces of cloth to the string or wool. Attach a small sign to each strip of cloth to explain what each marker symbolizes. You may wish to use stakes to keep each of these stages easily visible and off the ground. Notice how little of the earth's "life story" has to do with humans. Also, it was only after the industrial revolution that we even began to realize the negative effects that humans can have on the environment.

4. Invite a group of friends to walk through your timeline as you explain each marker.

# E.2 DESIGN AN ACCORDION-TYPE BOOKLET

Choose your favourite myth and write it in your own words for a younger audience. Present your illustrated myth in an accordion-type booklet following the directions below. Use **Tools C2** and **C8** to edit your work.

**MATERIALS REQUIRED**
- four illustrations measuring 9 cm x 9 cm
- scissors
- a legal-sized folder (37 cm long)
- felt pens, pens, or pencil crayons
- adhesive tape
- **Tool D1** (for evaluation criteria)

**DIRECTIONS**

1. Trim the tabs from the folder. Fold each side of the folder inwards to line up with the centre fold. Cut along each fold line to create four equal-sized strips.

2. Fold each strip like an accordion to make four panels. Attach two strips together with adhesive tape to make eight panels. (You can add other strips if necessary.) Decide which side of the strip will be the inside of the booklet.

3. On the first inside panel of the booklet, write the first part of your legend. Glue your image onto the next panel. Continue with your legend on the third panel, alternating a writing panel with a picture panel. Of course, you might want to change this format to have more panels with writing or more panels with pictures. It's up to you to decide.

4. Once you have finished step 3, close up your booklet by folding it together. Illustrate the front cover. Be sure to write the title of your legend and your name as the author on the cover.

5. If you wish, you could also add a border to each page. You might also decide to use the back side of your booklet.

# E.3 A PUPPET'S VIEW OF EARTH'S LIFE STORY

Tell the life story of the earth in a short play using puppets. In your play, have each puppet talk about how it appeared on Earth and what the earth was like at that time. Use the timeline from **STEPSpage 112** and **Tool D7** to help you with the dialogue for your play. Design a puppet or puppets for each of the stages shown on the timeline. For additional ideas, consult **E.4 Life's Woolly Web of Interrelationships** on **STEPSpage 116**.

– How could you dramatize each of the stages described?

– What different backgrounds would you need for your play?

– Should they be fixed backgrounds or moving ones? Moving backgrounds could be designed on bamboo skewers or some other stick.

There are many other geological or historical events that could be added to your presentation.

In preparing your presentation, refer to **Tools B2** and **A6** for help on dividing the tasks and preparing your performance.

**C**

A World of Legends

**C.3**

*Myths from the Beginning*

46 billion years ago

# E.4 LIFE'S WOOLLY WEB OF INTERRELATIONSHIPS

### MATERIALS REQUIRED

- a ball of wool
- a copy of the cards on **STEPSpage 118**

### DIRECTIONS

1. For this game you will need 12 players. Give each player a copy of one of the cards shown on **STEPSpage 118**.

2. Have the 12 players sit in a circle around a table. Ask each player to tell the others what is written on his or her card.

3. Once each player has read a card, the cards are placed face up on the table. The person with the "sun" card acts as the starter and holds the loose end of the ball of wool until the end of the game.

4. The object of the game is to form a web with the ball of wool or string by connecting all of the cards together. The "sun" person starts the web by explaining how the sun is important to another element in the circle. Example: "The angle of the sun's rays on the earth determines the seasons." The "sun" would then pass the ball of wool to the person representing the "seasons" (or whichever card was mentioned).

5. The player receiving the ball of wool then explains how his or her card relates to some other element in the circle and passes the ball of wool to the player representing the card mentioned.

6. It is important to note that once players have spoken, they too become anchor people, holding onto the wool and keeping the web's shape until the end of the game, where everyone is holding a part of the web. At the end, the players stand and walk once around the circle, keeping the web taut the entire time. How does this moving web represent the balance between Earth and the elements which impact on it?

To evaluate your success with following the directions for this game, see **Tool C7**. If you find it difficult to describe the connections between the different elements in the game, review the problem-solving process described in **Tool A1**.

**E.4 LIFE'S WOOLLY WEB OF INTERRELATIONSHIPS,** continued...

Copy the following twelve cards and glue them onto cardboard so that they are visible from a distance of about two metres.

**Sun**
I give light and energy so that plants may grow.

**Plants**
We use light to create food and oxygen.

**Soil and Rocks**
We contain the minerals and salts needed by all living things.

**Air**
I give the breath of air that all living things need.

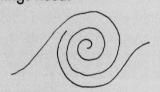

**Water**
I quench the thirst of all living things.

**Seasons**
Spring, fall, summer, winter bring constant changes to the earth.

**Animals**
We bring movement to the earth, helping plants to reproduce and feeding others.

**Stars and Moon**
We brighten the night sky and guide the humans and animals at night. I, the moon, control the tides.

**Humans**
We take care of the earth. We are responsible for the health of the earth.

**Legends**
We tell the tales of the earth. We are the creativity of the earth.

**Life and Death**
We bring about changes on Earth, adding life where there is none, or making room for new life.

**The Circle**
I keep life in motion so that it can never become stagnant. I make certain that there is balance.

LA: Identify/use information from a text to establish relationships of cause and effect and consequences and to question the premises for them.

SS: Understand how humans attempt to make sense of their environment through the expression of values and symbolism.

SD: Identify, develop, and sustain means of improving individual/group: understanding of cause and effect and repercussions; rights and responsibilities as members of a society or group.

Often myths, folktales, legends, and fables are used to teach the values of a cultural group. Courage, determination, patience, and respect are only a few of the valued traits explored in cultural folktales. Recurring themes found in folktales around the world are called **universal themes**. Some examples of universal themes found in many stories are "good conquers evil", "the weak overpower the mighty", and "the poor outsmart the rich".

Using **Tool A3** and your previous work in this centre, brainstorm a list of at least ten different folktales, myths, legends, and fables you know well. Beside each tale listed, describe the problem and how it was resolved. You need only use a few words for this. Make your description of the solution as general as possible. What universal theme would best describe this problem and its solution?

LA: Identify/use information from a text to establish relationships of cause and effect and consequences and to question the premises for them.

SS: Understand how humans attempt to make sense of their environment through the expression of values and symbolism.

SD: Identify, develop, and sustain means of improving individual/group: understanding of cause and effect and repercussions; rights and responsibilities as members of a society or group.

To explore other universal themes and lessons taught by tales, read at least two of the myths, legends, and folktales on **pages 29** to **48** of *Discovering Culture and Values*. For each tale, answer the questions on **STEPSpages 122, 123**. Note that **page 48** is not a tale but a painting. However, a tale could easily be told about this painting, especially when you consider its title, **"The Fortune-Teller"**.

.1 LA: Identify/use information from a text to establish relationships of cause and effect and consequences and to question the premises for them.

SS: Understand how humans attempt to make sense of their environment through the expression of values and symbolism.

SD: Identify, develop, and sustain means of improving individual/group: understanding of cause and effect and repercussions; rights and responsibilities as members of a society or group.

Select one of the tales read during the activity stage. Rewrite this tale so that it takes place in your community and reflects the strengths valued by the members of your community. You will probably need to change the setting, the time period, the characters, and some of their traits or their expressions. If these tales are too difficult to adapt to your region, choose another tale that would adapt more easily. See **Tool C8** to edit your work.

**Or**

.2 LA: Identify/use information from a text to establish relationships of cause and effect and consequences and to question the premises for them.

SS: Understand how humans attempt to make sense of their environment through the expression of values and symbolism.

SD: Identify, develop, and sustain means of improving individual/group: understanding of cause and effect and repercussions; rights and responsibilities as members of a society or group.

Change the point of view from which a tale is told. There are many excellent examples of traditional tales told from another point of view. **The Three Little Wolves and the Big Bad Pig** by Eugene Trivizas and Helen Oxbury or **The True Story of the Three Little Pigs! By A. Wolf** as told by Jon Scieszka are just two examples of how the story. **The Three Little Pigs** could be told from a different point of view.

**Or**

.3 LA: Identify/use information from a text to establish relationships of cause and effect and consequences and to question the premises for them.

SS: Understand how humans attempt to make sense of their environment through the expression of values and symbolism.

SD: Identify, develop, and sustain means of improving individual/group: understanding of cause and effect and repercussions; rights and responsibilities as members of a society or group.)

Fairytales, nursery rhymes, folktales, and other stories often contain remarks or illustrations which reinforce stereotypes and other misconceptions about a cultural group. **Hansel and Gretel** is a wonderful tale, but you cannot conclude from it that all German girls have long blond braids and that all the boys wear *Lederhosen* (leather shorts). Little Red Riding Hood may have brought red wine and a baguette to her grandmother in the forest, but this doesn't mean that all children in France run through the forests with baskets of bread and wine. To better understand how ridiculous generalized statements can be, play the game on **STEPSpages 124, 125**.

LA: Identify/use information from a text to establish relationships of cause and effect and consequences and to question the premises for them.

SS: Understand how humans attempt to make sense of their environment through the expression of values and symbolism.

SD: Identify, develop, and sustain means of improving individual/group: understanding of cause and effect and repercussions; rights and responsibilities as members of a society or group.

Using **Tool A1**, describe one example of a universal theme and give at least three examples of tales you know which develop this theme. For each example, describe how the universal theme is developed. Conclude your description with a statement to explain why this theme is a universal one and is accepted and valued in many countries. How do universal themes help societies work together?

# C

## A World of Legends

## C.4

### Lessons to be Learned

 TALES AND LEGENDS

What important lessons are contained in the legends and tales on **pages 29** to **48** of *Discovering Culture and Values*? After reading at least two of these tales, answer the questions below. For a list of general questions to explore your understanding of these tales, see **Tool C1**.

1. What is the universal theme, or message, that each tale tries to pass on to its readers? Give two examples to justify your choice of theme for each tale. (It is not the "right" answer that is important here, but rather that you can interpret a tale and give your reasons for your interpretation.)

2. What strengths do the characters in these tales possess? How do they use these strengths to resolve their problems? (Examples of strengths often valued by a cultural group are: courage, curiosity, endurance, physical strength, beauty, intelligence, empathy for others, etc.)

3. What challenges are described in the tale? How are these challenges overcome? (Examples of challenges might be: fear, ignorance, greed, weakness, etc.)

4. Do you believe that certain choices we make in our lives affect other people, animals, plants, or the earth? Give examples of choices in these tales that affected others.

5. What choices do the individuals in these tales make that keep their society or their families strong for future generations? Give examples.

6. Select the tales you read and answer the specific questions below:

   – What personality traits did Oumpah possess that earned him the respect of the other animals? (See **p. 29** of *Discovering Culture and Values*.)

   – What traits did the serpent show at the end of the story? (See **p. 29**.)

   – How does this description of fire and ice match with science's explanation of the creation of the world? (See **p. 34**.)

   – In our world of electric lights, perhaps we, too, live in a world of never-ending daylight. What happens to plants and animals when they don't get enough darkness and time to rest? (See **p. 38**.)

# TALES AND LEGENDS, continued...

- What are the three different parts of the sacred pipe? What does each part represent? (See **p. 41**.)

- Sometimes lessons which seem of little use at the time become invaluable at a later date. Why were Tokoyo's life experiences so important in helping her father? (See **p. 44**.)

- What did the quest for the lion's whiskers symbolize? Were the whiskers really important or was there something more important in this story? (See **p. 46**.)

- What is the story this artist is telling? Viewers will have different opinions and unless you talk with the artist, it is impossible to know the "right" answer. So instead of a right answer, describe what the painting is saying to you and explain your ideas. (See **p. 48**.)

## E.3 EXPOSING THE STEREOTYPES

Fairytales, nursery rhymes, folktales, and other stories often contain remarks or illustrations that reinforce stereotypes and other misconceptions about a cultural group. To better understand how ridiculous generalizations can be, play the game described below. You will need several small squares of paper, a hat, and a small bag to use as a garbage bag. Books of legends, tales, or stories from a variety of cultures would be useful in creating your list of traits.

Begin by writing down a list of countries and the name, or names, of the cultural groups living in these countries. Then, on small squares of paper, write a description of a personality trait (intelligent, easily angered), a type of clothing, a food dish, or some other trait that might be used to describe a person. Place the completed squares in a hat or bag.

Each player takes a turn selecting the name of a cultural group and then drawing a trait square from the hat. Using these two pieces of information, the player completes this sentence: "All _____ (cultural group name) are/wear/eat_____."

The other players in the group decide whether to accept or challenge the statement being made. If the statement is accepted, the trait goes back into the hat. If the statement is challenged, the trait is torn up and dropped in the garbage. To challenge a statement, players use phrases like: "You must be mistaken. I have a friend who is (cultural group) and who…" or "I disagree with your generalization of this culture because…" or "I consider your remark insulting and I think you should apologize for making it", etc.

From your collection of tales, you may find many examples of stereotypes, but you will also find books where the illustrator and the author have worked hard to avoid stereotyping the characters in their stories. After playing the game above, examine several illustrated tales to look for examples of stereotypes.

- What examples did you find? Describe why you think these are examples of stereotyping. Do the others in your discussion group agree with you?

- What are the publication dates of the books in which you found examples of stereotyping? Did you find more examples in recently published books or in older books?

- It is important to remember that our views of ourselves and of others change over time. Learning to recognize stereotypes is one step in the process. Working to counter stereotypes and to base our opinions on many experiences and viewpoints rather than on gossip and on generalizations is the more difficult step, but also the more rewarding one. Think of one stereotypical statement that you would like to see changed. How would you work to change it?

## Cooperative Learning Project

## A Celebration of Cultures

**Important notes**

1. The cultural celebration you are about to prepare is a culminating activity for this centre to show others what you have learned. **It is important that you complete the preparation stage at the start of your work with this centre**. The centre activities you select for inclusion in your cultural celebration will be influenced by your enthusiasm, numbers (as organizers), time, areas of interest and/or of study, and available space.

2. This project is a cooperative one. You will be working in teams to complete different tasks. Each team's quality contributions are essential to the success of the project.

3. If you would like to share your successes with others, please send a description of your project, along with copies of pictures, evaluations, etc., to: **Art Image Publications**. (See the copyright page for the address.)

SD: Identify, develop, sustain means of improving individual/group:
- acceptance of others' ideas
- interaction with others and with the environment
- organization and use of time
- roles, rights, responsibilities within a group
- decision-making and problem-solving skills
- ability to question/evaluate actions
- perseverance in spite of obstacles
- esteem, feelings of belonging and of value
- attributes (actual, potential, or desired)
- process skills: goal setting, planning, achieving, and evaluating)
- risk taking, motivation, autonomy, confidence

# PRE-CELEBRATION: PART 1. ESTABLISHING THE CONTENT

What is a cultural celebration? An excellent example is the **potlatch**, a West Coast Haida celebration. When a Haida family has acquired wealth through hard work and good fortune, it is customary for that family to host a potlatch. This celebration allows the family to share their wealth with others in their community and in surrounding communities. A potlatch may also be held for other special celebrations such as when a new chief is named or when a new member joins the family as in a marriage or a birth.

– What other cultural celebrations can you think of? What happens at these celebrations?

– What would you like to see in a cultural celebration?

– How will you share your wealth of knowledge about your culture with others?

– What special events/displays/presentations could be part of this celebration?

– Where could the celebration be held? (inside: school, house; outside: forest, etc.)

– How will you divide the total time available for the presentation? (opening ceremony, events, presentations, etc.)

– How will information be passed on during the celebration? (visuals, dialogue, lectures, etc.)

# PRE-CELEBRATION:
## PART 2. BRAINSTORMING IDEAS FOR A CULTURAL CELEBRATION

Examine the *Thoughtsteps Map* and **STEPSpages 128-129** to create a list of ideas that could be included in a cultural celebration of your own. Then divide your ideas into categories as shown on **STEPSpage 130**. As you complete the activities for this centre, remember that you will need to keep all your materials, visuals, props, and scripts from each activity for the cultural celebration at the end!

# FROM ORGANIZATION TO CELEBRATION

Before you begin preparations for your cultural celebration, you will need to refer to **Tool A6** and the list of ideas generated from the preparation stage, **STEPSpage 129**. See **STEPSpages 131** to **134** to explore the progressive stages in organizing your celebration.

**E.1** Examine creative ways to invite and welcome your guests.
See **STEPSpage 135**.

Or

**E.2** Compose, or select, the music to be used during your celebration.
See **Tool B3**.

Or

**E.3** Conduct a survey of the people attending your celebration. To prepare the questions for your survey, see **Tool A4**. To examine your survey results, see **Tools A3** or **D5** and **D6**.

# POST-CELEBRATION DISCUSSION

When the celebration is over, take time as a group to evaluate it, using **Tool A9** and the questions below. Record your answers in your *Thoughtsteps Journal*. See **STEPSpage 132**.

- Was the planning/organization of the celebration effective? How did you promote it?

- Did each individual or team contribute to the best of his/her/their ability?

- What problems did you encounter? What were your successes? What would you change?

- Were your participants enthusiastic about the celebration and did they receive your intended message?

- In another situation, how could you make use of what you learned?

**Cooperative Learning Project**

**A Celebration of Cultures**

### STEP 1: FAMILIARIZE YOURSELF WITH THE LEARNING ACTIVITIES IN THIS CENTRE

Examine the various learning activity paths on the *Thoughtsteps* Map. As you read through the map, write down the ideas you would like to include in a cultural celebration. To help you with this task, look at the list below. It provides a summary of the possible "end-products" that can be completed for each path on the map.

**Possible products from the learning activity paths in the *Discovering Culture and Values* centre.**
(For a better description of each of the suggestions listed below, see the *Thoughtsteps Map* and the explanations in **Steps to *Discovering Culture and Values*.**)

A.1 Survival game; invented game; collage, graph, interview, on endangered species; mobile of animals and their needs; visualization exercise about harmony; dance creation representing harmony in nature.

A.2 Poetry about early peoples and movement of populations; comparisons with First Nations peoples in other parts of the world; illustrations, research, poems of traditional and contemporary lifestyles of First Nations peoples; art and music from First Nations groups; study of lifestyle changes and environment.

A.3 Visual symbol representing the environment; collage of animal/plant life and impact of humans; environmental awareness poster; debate on an environmental issue; clay model of an animal; dance about problem menacing the environment.

A.4 Collage about interdependence; study of symbols in society; study of native art symbols; poem of life; survey of symbolism of colours.

A.5 Improvised dialogues about nature; skit about the living planet; mask creations; mime/dance using masks; mask parade.

B.1 Illustrations of local region 700 years ago; observations of art reproductions; model of early inhabitants' habitat and community; scrapbook or video of model scenes; model scene of local region in the future.

B.2 Illustrated descriptions of a journey to a new land; skit depicting journey to a new land; interview of reasons for leaving homeland to move to another country; television interview about reasons for leaving Canada; collage, sculpture, illustration or replica of a trunk packed for a journey; imaginary interview with a pioneer immigrating to Canada.

B.3 Creation of a new coat of arms; study of the symbolism in national and provincial coats of arms; survey of ancestry; creation of a personal coat of arms; study and map statistics for immigration and emigration.

B.4 Research on origin of names, cultural celebrations, traditions, or customs; survey of names in your school; descriptions of favourite customs, holidays; study of cultural place names; research on languages spoken in Canada.

B.5 Diary about encounters with people contributing to Canada; mural of famous Canadians and their contributions/inventions; collection of stories about contributing Canadians; study of a Canadian inventor; study of traditional and contemporary Canadian music; imaginary plans for a summer vacation across Canada; chart of famous Canadians who reached their goals.

C.1 Writing about a legend to explore how they are created; skit about the origin of rain; study of cultural values/symbols in legends; character cube of a legendary hero; maze of different legends; modernized version of a legend.

C.2 Improvisations of legends or myths; play about a legend or tale; mask creations; songs about legends.

C.3 Cultural comparisons of legends and tales; timeline of the earth's story; thinking game to explore connections; puppet play of the earth's life story; storybook of a myth.

C.4 Descriptions of universal themes in tales; comparisons of cultural universal themes; adapted tales for local communities; tales from a different point of view; game about stereotypes.

### STEP 2: DECIDE ON THE FOCUS MESSAGE OF YOUR CULTURAL CELEBRATION

As a group, discuss your ideas for this cultural celebration from the list you drew up during **Step 1**. Probably the most difficult part in your preparation is to reach an agreement on the focus message for your cultural celebration.

– What is your celebration about? (e.g., How will you describe it to others?)

– What message would you like to leave with your participants?

– After attending your cultural celebration, how would you like your participants to describe it to someone who was not able to be there?

Prepare a chart as shown on the following page. Write in the focus message for your cultural celebration so that everyone organizing the celebration may refer to it often. Then, select the activities from the centre which will best allow you to deliver your message. Enter your selections in the appropriate columns below. Later, while working in the centre, you may decide to add new components to the celebration, or delete inappropriate ones. Always remember to refer to your focus message before making any changes.

**Cooperative Learning Project**

*A Celebration of Cultures*

### FOCUS MESSAGE FOR THIS CULTURAL CELEBRATION

### THIS CULTURAL CELEBRATION WILL DELIVER THE ABOVE MESSAGE TO ITS PARTICIPANTS BY USING THE FOLLOWING APPROACHES:
(Select from the activities below and list your selections in one of the columns here.)

| informative cultural displays | audience entertainment (plays, songs, etc.) | "how to..." demonstrations | audience participation activities (debates, discussions, games, etc.) |
|---|---|---|---|
| | | | |

**Important Reminder!!!**
As you complete the activities for this centre, remember to keep all the materials, visuals, props, and scripts for your culminating activity, the cultural celebration!

# PRE-CELEBRATION PREPARATIONS

**1. ESTABLISH THE FORMAT FOR YOUR CULTURAL CELEBRATION.**

1.1 After working through the different activities in *Discovering Culture and Values*, you are now ready to look back at the initial plans made during the preparation stage. Refer to your completed planning chart from **STEPSpage 129**. In small groups, use this chart and the questions from **Tool A6** to discuss your ideas and plans for an "ideal" cultural celebration. **It is important to focus on the message of your celebration.**

1.2 Present your group's ideas and plans to the other teams involved in the celebration. While listening to each team's proposals, take notes on the ideas presented. To write your notes quickly, divide this task among the members of your team according to the sections mentioned in **Tool A6**.

1.3 Once every team has presented its ideas, develop a collective outline of the format of your celebration, including as many of the ideas from each group's proposal as possible. You will need to use **Tool A6** once again to develop this outline.

**2. PREPARE THE INDIVIDUAL ACTION PLANS AND TASK LISTS; THEN PREPARE THE GROUP PLAN.**

2.1 To prepare the action plan for the cultural celebration, it's easiest to first have each team prepare its action plan, complete with a list of the tasks to be completed for its own portion of the celebration.

2.2 Once each team has completed its portion of the celebration plan, the work needs to be shared with the other teams involved in preparing the event.

2.3 Together, make any final changes before posting the group action plan and task list. See **STEPSpage 129**.

2.4 Next, review the job descriptions on **STEPSpage 132** and divide your celebration organizers into committees. (Remember that there is an assumption here that everyone is already a member of a group with a presentation ready for inclusion in the celebration.) The presentation groups need to have a representative on each organizing committee. Each committee will be responsible for completing one section of the task list and for providing the expertise in their field (event descriptions, event layout, event materials).

2.5 Throughout the preparation process, you will need to have constant "reality checks" with your organizing committee and also with your presentation partners. When you are ready to present the celebration, see the instructions on **STEPSpage 133-134**.

**Are you ready for this? Good luck!**

# CELEBRATION COMMITTEES: JOB DESCRIPTIONS

| COMMITTEE | RESPONSIBILITIES |
|---|---|
| **Adjudicators** | This is a special committee apart from the three others. It is made up of a small number of students and the facilitator. This committee's job is to review the celebration events and to ensure that each event is of high quality. |
| **Publicity/Public Relations Officers** | **Pre-event:** prepare and distribute publicity, announcements, invitations<br>**Event:** perform opening/ closing ceremonies, make announcements, conduct surveys, explain the hands-on activities or events<br>**Post-event:** report and analyze roles |
| **Architects/Construction Crew/ Technicians** | **Pre-event:** prepare scale drawings of the celebration area; consult with presentation groups to establish what props and display space are needed for each presentation; construct and place props/equipment; organize display and presentation areas for maximum effect and for ease of movement/circulation/presentation<br>**Event:** prepare lighting, special effects, music, and technical equipment; control movement of people, demonstrate activities and events<br>**Post-event:** report and analyze roles |
| **Layout/Graphic Artists** | **Pre-event:** prepare detailed scale drawings of the contents of each display or performance area; consult with architects/technicians to establish layout needs; prepare signs/banners/backdrops for the presentations; organize and supervise the layout of the displays<br>**Event:** explain visual displays; supervise display areas<br>**Post-event:** report and analyze roles |

# POST-CELEBRATION DISCUSSION (This process is done as a whole group.)

1. Each organizing committee reports on how well the roles were assumed.

2. The cultural celebration event is reviewed and criticized for the effectiveness of its message.

3. Feedback from the participants is discussed to learn whether the focus message was received and understood. This feedback is also valuable in determining how to improve future projects.

# ORGANIZE THE VARIOUS LAYOUTS FOR YOUR CELEBRATION

The main purpose of preparing good visual layout plans for publicity and for your celebration performance and display areas is to enable several people to work toward a common goal. If the layout plans are well prepared and are posted in a visible place, several people could work together at the same time to construct props or paint banners or prepare the performance set designs.

## PRINT/VISUAL PUBLICITY

Measure the dimensions of your poster, your invitation, or your publicity display area. Decide on the sizes for your lettering using your calculations for space. Draw fine guidelines across your poster with a pencil. Using graph paper to draw your draft version allows you to create small announcements and large posters from the same copy. See **Tools D4** and **D9**.

## ARCHITECTS

Measure the dimensions of the areas where you plan to host the celebration and prepare a scale drawing by referring to **Tool D4**. Your large props, displays, and so on also need to be illustrated on your plan. When preparing your plan, it is important to consider how the visitors will move from one area to the next. It is also important to group your displays and presentations with a purpose.

To do this, you need to consider the types of messages/impressions you want your visitors to experience and how to deliver these messages/impressions throughout the display areas.

– Are there times during the celebrations where everyone needs to come together? Will your space be suitable for this?

– What opening message/experience/impression do you want to present to your visitors?

– What do you expect your visitors to observe, learn, and do throughout the celebration?

– What message/impression/experience do you want to leave with your visitors?

If you are really energetic, you can even prepare a miniature model of your cultural celebration area by constructing tables, stands, theatrical backdrops, etc., from rectangular or triangular prisms. See **Tool E7**.

Cooperative Learning Project

## A Celebration of Cultures

## Cooperative Learning Project

### *A Celebration of Cultures*

# ORGANIZE THE VARIOUS LAYOUTS FOR YOUR CELEBRATION, continued...

**GRAPHIC ARTISTS**

Measure the dimensions of your display and presentation areas. Be creative with available space by thinking about how you can best use your floor space, the ceiling, the walls, and available furniture. Use inventions like panels on tabletops or freestanding coat racks with revolving boxes for displaying information. Think about how you want visitors to move through your displays or where you want them to be during performances. What do you want them to focus on? How will you get their attention?

– What opening message/experience/impression do you want your visitors to have?

– What do you expect your visitors to observe, learn, or do in your presentation area? Is this obvious to the visitors?

– What message/impression/experience do you want to leave with your visitors?

– Is your display/presentation appealing to your visitors? Is it of professional quality?

Prepare your layout ideas on graph paper so that you can later divide among other members of your team the tasks of colouring, posting, and arranging. Refer to **Tool D4** for help with graphic layouts.

**.1 EXAMINE CREATIVE WAYS TO INVITE AND WELCOME YOUR GUESTS**

Before you invite your guests to your cultural celebration, discuss how people are attracted to or invited to events in your area. Brainstorm a list of ideas. See **Tool A2**. To support your ideas, give examples of written and graphic publicity, television advertising, and radio announcements you have viewed or listened to. What do you remember most about the announcement? What words, images, sounds, colours, and shapes come to mind when you recall the details of the publicity?

From your list of ideas, identify the publicity techniques best suited to your purpose: to announce your cultural celebration. In your *Thoughtsteps Journal*, write a list of points or details to consider when preparing the publicity. See **Tool D3**.

Select the publicity formats you will use for your celebration. Or, use these ideas to come up with something even more creative! Using **Tools D9** and **C8**, design your celebration announcement.

With the ideas from your publicity, design a welcoming souvenir for your cultural celebration or for a particular display, activity, or demonstration at your cultural celebration. This might be a multicultural bookmark, an illustrated program pamphlet, the focus message in the form of a poem, a wallet card, or…

When your guests arrive at your cultural celebration, how will you receive them? Will they be presented with your gift, memory of the event, souvenir, or symbol of the celebration at the start of the event? How will you make them feel welcome? Using **Tool A2**, brainstorm a list of ideas in keeping with your celebration.

# DISCOVERING CULTURE AND VALUES

## REFERENCE BOOKS

Abeles, Joan. **Places to Go, People to See, Things to Do All Across Canada.** Scholastic, 1994. ISBN: 0-590-74550-6.

Bevan Turner, Dolby. **When the Rains Came and Other Legends of the Salish People.** Orca Book Publishers, 1992. ISBN: 0-920501-87-7.

Bruchac, Joseph & Caduto, Michael J. **Native American Animal Stories.** Fulcrum Publishing, 1992. ISBN: 1-55591-127-7.

Caduto, Michael & Bruchac, Joseph. **Keepers of the Animals: Native Stories and Wildlife Activities for Children.** Fulcrum Publishing, 1991. ISBN: 0-92007-988-1.

Caduto, Michael & Bruchac, Joseph. **Keepers of the Earth: Native Stories and Environmental Activities for Children.** Fulcrum Publishing, 1991. ISBN: 0-92007-957-1.

Cameron, Anne. **Raven and Snipe.** Harbour Publishing, 1992. ISBN: 1-55017-037-6.

Challand, Helen. **Vanishing Forest.** Chicago Children's Press, 1991. ISBN: 0-516-05505-4.

De Vas, Gail & Harris, Merle. **Telling Tales, Story-telling in the Family.** Dragon Hill Publications, 1995. ISBN: 1-896124-01-1.

Eisen, Arman. **A Treasury of Children's Literature.** Houghton Mifflin, 1992. ISBN: 0-395-53349-X.

Francis, Lee. **Native Time: Historical Timeline of North America.** St. Martin, 1996. ISBN: 0-312-13129-1.

Halpin, Marjorie. **Totem Poles, an Illustrated Guide.** UBC Press, 1991. ISBN: 0-7748-0141-7.

Harrison, Ted. **O Canada.** Kids Can Press, 1992. ISBN: 1-55074-087-3.

Henley, Thom. **Rediscovery: Ancient Pathways, New Directions.** Outdoor activities based on native traditions. Lone Pine Publications, 1996. ISBN: 1-55105-077-3.

Hughes, Monica. **A Handful of Seeds.** Orchard Books, 1996. ISBN: 0-531-09498-7.

Hughes, Monica. **Gold Fever Trail.** Stoddart Publications, 1990. ISBN: 0-7736-7279-6

Jones, Charlotte Foltz. **Mistakes That Worked.** Doubleday, 1991. ISBN: 0-385-32043-4.

Keens-Douglas, Ricardo. **The Nutmeg Princess.** Annick Press, 1992. ISBN: 1-44037-239-4.

Kherdian, David. **Feathers and Tails: Animal Fables from Around the World.** Philomel Books, 1992. ISBN: 0-399-21876-9.

Knudtson, Peter & Suzuki, David. **The Wisdom of the Elders.** Stoddart, 1992. ISBN: 0-7737-2520-2.

Kusugaak, Michael. **Northern Lights: The Soccer Trails.** Annick Press, 1993. ISBN: 1-555037-3390.

Lawson, Julie. **Too Many Suns.** Stoddart, 1996. 0-7737-2897-X.

Lawson, Julie. **Blown Away.** Red Deer College Press, 1995. 0-88995-119-5.

Lawson, Julie. **White Jade Tiger.** Beach Holme Publications, 1993. 0-88878-333-7.

Lottridge, Celia. **The Name of the Tree.** Oxford University Press, 1989. ISBN: 19-540843-8.

Malarek, Victor. **Haven's Gate: Canada's Immigration Fiasco.** Macmillan, 1987. ISBN: 0-7715-9497-6.

McClintock, Barbara. **Animal Fables from Aesop.** David R. Goldine, 1991. ISBN: 0-87923-913-1.

McGugan, Jim. **Josepha, a Prairie Boy's Story.** Red Deer College Press, 1994. ISBN: 0-88995-101-2.

Millman, Lawrence. **Wolverine Creates the World: Labrador Indian Tales.** Capra Press, 1993. ISBN: 0-88496-393-2.

Mollel, Tololwa. **An African Story, a Promise to the Sun.** Little, Brown, & Co., 1992. ISBN: 0-316-57813-4.

Mollel, Tololwa. **The Orphan Boy.** Oxford University Press, 1990. ISBN: 19-540783-0.

Muller, Robin. **The Magic Paintbrush.** Doubleday, 1992. ISBN: 0-38525-373-7.

Mutel, Cornelia & Rodger, Mary. **Our Endangered Planet: Tropical Rainforests.** Lerner Publications, 1991. ISBN: 0-8225-2503.

New, W.H. **Native Writers and Canadian Writing.** UBC Press, 1990. ISBN: 0-7748-0371-1.

Opie, Iona & Opie, Peter. **I Saw Esau: The Schoolchild's Pocket Book of Rhymes and Riddles.** Candlewick Press, 1992. ISBN: 1-56402-046-0.

Pekarik, Andrew. **Sculpture: Behind the Scenes.** Hyperion, 1992. ISBN: 1-56282-295-0.

Rodanas, Kristina. **Eagle's Song: A Tale from the Pacific North-West.** Little, 1995. ISBN: 0-316-75375-0.

Rodanas, Kristina. **Dance of the Sacred Circle.** Little, 1994. ISBN: 0-316-75358-0.

Schwartz, Alvin. **And the Green Grass Grew All Around: Folk Poetry from Everyone.** HarperCollins, 1992. ISBN: 0-06-022758-3.

Scieszka, Jon. **The True Story of the Three Little Pigs! By A. Wolf.** Scholastic, 1989. ISBN: 0-590-44357-7.

Singh, Manmohan & Minhas, Moni. **The Sikh Canadians.** Reidmore Books, 1994. ISBN: 1-895073-44-8.

Taylor, C.J. **The Monster from the Swamp.** Tundra Books, 1995. ISBN: 0-88776-361-8.

Taylor, C.J. **Little Water and the Gift of the Animals.** Tundra Books, 1992. ISBN: 0-88776-285-9.

Taylor, C.J. **How Two-Feather Was Saved From Loneliness.** Tundra Books, 1990. ISBN: 0-88776-254-9.

Taylor, Colin. **Native American Myths and Legends.** Cavendish Books, 1994. ISBN: 0-929050-57-6.

Terzian, Alexandra M. **The Kids' Multicultural Art Book: Art & Craft Experiences from Around the World.** Williamson Pub. Co., 1993. ISBN: 0-913589-72-1.

Thomas, Chief Jacob. **Teachings from the Longhouse.** Stoddart, 1994. ISBN: 0-7737-5659-0.

Trivizas, Eugene & Oxenbury, Helen. **The Three Little Wolves and the Big Bad Pig.** Scholastic, 1993. ISBN: 0-590-48622-5.

Valgardson, Bill. **Sarah and the People of Sand River.** Groundwood Books, 1996. ISBN: 0-88899-255-6.

Yee, Paul. **Ghost Train.** Groundwood Books, 1996. ISBN: 0-88899-257-2.

Yee, Paul. **Roses Sing on New Snow.** Groundwood Books, 1991. ISBN: 0-88899-144-4.

## MULTIMEDIA

**World Vista Multimedia Atlas.** Applied Optical Media Corporation. Mac (CMAPO21061) or Win (CMAPO20131).

**World Atlas Version 5.0.** The Software Toolworks. Mac (CMSTL11670).

**Art First Nations, Kit 1.** Art Image Publications, 1992. ISBN: 2-921370-90-5.

**Art First Nations, Kit 2.** Art Image Publications, 1992. ISBN: 2-921370-91-3.

## VIDEOS

**Spirits of the Rainforest.** Discovery Video Library, 1993. CD23627. (Machiguenga Indians: their myths, legends, and legacies.)

## MUSIC

Among artists whose music you might want to listen to are:

| | |
|---|---|
| The Chieftains | Glenn Gould |
| Valdy | Susan Aglukark |
| Gordon Lightfoot | The Rankin Family |
| Joni Mitchell | |

## OTHER ADDRESSES FOR RESOURCES

Baffin Tourism Association, PO Box 1450, Iqaluit, NWT, X0A 0H0

Batoche Natural Historic Park, PO Box 999, Rosthern, SK, S0K 3R0

Canadian Museum of Civilization, 100 rue Laurier, CP 3100, Succ. B, Hull, QC, J8X 4H2

Centre Culturel Franco-Manitobain, 340 boul. Provencher, St. Boniface, MB, R2H 0G7

Fortress of Louisbourg, PO Box 160, Louisbourg, NS, B0A 1M0

Historic Acadian Village, PO Box 820, Caraquet, NB, E0B 1K0

Holocaust Memorial Centre, 5151 ch. Côte-Ste-Catherine, Montréal, QC, H3W 1M6

Kahnawake Social Services Centre, Box 927, Kahnawake, QC, J0L 1B0

King's Landing Historical Settlement, PO Box 522, Fredericton, NB, E3B 5A6

L'Anse-aux-Meadows National Historic Park, PO Box 70, St. Lunaire-Griguet, NF, A0K 2X0

Musée du Québec, 1 av. Montcalm, Battlefields Park, QC, G1R 5H3

Museum of Anthropology, 6393 NW Marine Drive, Vancouver, BC, V6T 1Z2

Ndilo Cultural Village, Yellowknife Band Office, PO Box 2514, Yellowknife, NWT, X1A 2P8

North American Black Historical Museum and Cultural Centre, 277 King St., PO Box 12, Amherstburg, ON, N9V 2C7

Nova Scotia Highland Village, PO Box 58, Iona, NS, B0A 1L0

Ukrainian Cultural Heritage Village, 8820 – 112 Street, Edmonton, AB, T6G 2P8

Upper Canada Village, RR1 Morrisburg, ON, K0C 1X0

Wanuskewin Heritage Park, RR4 Saskatoon, SK, S7K 3J7